RUNNING WITH CURVES

WHY YOU'RE NOT TOO FAT TO RUN, AND THE SKINNY ON HOW TO START TODAY

Jill Angie

Cover and Interior Design: John H. Matthews
Editing: Kris Kane

TABLE OF CONTENTS

This book is dedicated to my husband, Ken, for believing in my wildest dreams and helping me bring them to life.
Thank you.

FOREWORD

When I first sat down to write this book in September 2013, my intention was to create a running primer for overweight women, essentially a how-to for those that most running books leave behind. Along the way, however, it became so much more than that. A manifesto of sorts, letting the world know that running is not just for the slim, svelte or slender. That in fact, women of all shapes, sizes and ages can become runners - and that their lives will be irrevocably changed in the process.

And so I created the book I wish had existed when I started running 17 years ago. A shortcut past all the bullshit mind tricks, self-shaming and other shenanigans I put myself through on my journey from fat and frumpy to fit and fabulous.

What I didn't realize, however, was that I was also writing the book I'd need a year or so later.

After Running With Curves was published, I started getting emails and Facebook messages from my readers: they saw themselves in my words, and they felt heard. Validated. No longer alone. I created a private Facebook group so these amazing women could connect directly with each other, and suddenly…a movement was born. An army of curvy women, standing in their power, encouraging and supporting one another to even greater heights.

At the same time, my own passion for running begin to wane. The pressure to stand as an example of what was possible became overwhelming, and my poor lonely running shoes sat by the front door, unused for weeks. Running began to feel like work, and I felt like a complete fraud. How could I lead the running revolution when putting on my running shoes was the last thing I wanted to do?

Fortunately, I made the decision to expand this book beyond the Kindle platform, which prompted me to reread it in detail. With a beginner's mind, I heard my own words reflected back at me:

"It doesn't matter how many times you start over, as long as you do".

And suddenly, it was all OK.

My deepest wish for you is that you'll be changed after you finish reading Running With Curves. That you'll see yourself a little differently, with compassion. As someone who runs on her own terms, in a way that feels joyous, confident and empowered. No longer defining yourself as a fat runner, an overweight runner, or even a slow runner. Just a runner like any other, embracing the highs and lows, enjoying the journey, perhaps even sharing her passion with the rest of the world. You never know who you might inspire.

Run fabulous,
Jill Angie
February 25th, 2015

ABOUT THIS BOOK

"Run when you can, walk if you have to, crawl if you must; just never give up."
Dean Karnazes

If you're reading this book, I assume you either want to learn more about running or you accidentally clicked the "Buy now" button on your Kindle and you're silently cursing your itchy trigger finger. Regardless of the reason, here we are and I think we've got a lot to discuss.

First of all, what is this book about? On the surface, it's about running. Specifically, how a woman carrying a few (or many) extra pounds can successfully become a runner in the body she has, right now. But this is also a book about side effects. Running is addictive, and after you've been doing it for a while, people will begin to notice undeniable changes in your behavior. They might not say anything to your face, but behind your back they'll be talking:

"She just seems so much more confident lately–do you think she's had work done?"

"Perhaps it's a new pair of heels? Lately she just seems … taller."

"Maybe she's having an affair. Three times a week, she disappears at lunch and comes back looking so satisfied. And a little sweaty."

Confidence: a classic side-effect of a running addiction.

But I digress. First, we need to chat about obesity, self-esteem, and Pinterest. Trust me–they are related.

It's no secret that waistlines are growing. Walk down any street and you'll see plenty of people who meet the medical definition of obese. This phenomenon isn't limited to the US–the world is growing larger, and the trend doesn't appear to be slowing. Experts point to numerous causes: poor diets that rely too much on convenience (usually processed) foods, enormous portions, sprawling suburbs set up for driving instead of walking, and even the diet industry itself. And they're right–these issues are all part of the problem, along with dozens more that I haven't named.

But there is another fundamental contributor, something that most people overlook when trying to understand why we are busting out of our clothes, airplane seats and restaurant chairs: self-esteem, or rather, the lack of it among women and girls in this country.

You could argue that low self-esteem is a symptom of the obesity epidemic, rather than the cause. I agree, to a point, but it's more like the chicken and the egg–which came first? We'll probably never know, and it doesn't really matter. Low self-esteem and obesity are inextricably linked in our society.

Judging and shaming others for their physical imperfections has become a national pastime. Don't believe me? Pick up any tabloid and you're guaranteed to see photos of a Hollywood star who has dared to publicly frolic in a bikini, brazenly exposing two square inches of cellulite on an otherwise perfect butt. This phenomenon isn't limited to those in the public eye. A quick look at Instagram or Facebook will almost certainly yield snapshots of overweight and/or oddly dressed people, accompanied by a snidely worded status update mocking them. Why? If you're feeling fat, ugly, or in any way *less than perfect* yourself, it's easy to look at someone else's body or sense of style and think "I may have flaws, but at least I don't look like *that*."

But as cruel as women can be when judging others, we never criticize anyone more harshly than ourselves. If your girlfriend gains five pounds, you console her with something like "Don't worry, it's only water weight." But if you do the same? The little voice inside your head is more likely to sound something like "You lazy piece of crap, you're a complete failure at life." If you think I'm exaggerating, eavesdrop on your internal dialogue sometime. I mean *really* listen. You'll be shocked at what you say to yourself. If your best friend spoke to you that way, your friendship wouldn't last long—so why is it OK to treat yourself so poorly?

We're constantly told that being overweight is a character flaw, and we believe it. We claim it as truth, as factual as the color of our eyes or the size of our feet. The earth is round. Being fat makes you a terrible person.

Obsession with perfection is everywhere: magazines, TV, internet, billboards, social media. The messages are insidious, and before we realize what's happened, the thought "You don't measure up" becomes an unshakable truth. We understand that the flawless images we see everywhere are a result of good lighting and Photoshop, but those nasty, whispery voices in our heads have already bought into the dogma of perfection with gusto, and they are not afraid to speak up and make their opinions heard.

So we spend hours and hours perusing websites like Pinterest and Facebook, painstakingly searching for inspiration and advice to help us come closer to the standard of perfection. Posting photos of extremely fit women as fitness inspiration (or as the practice is commonly known, Fitspiration) seems like an innocuous, perhaps even useful, pastime. What's wrong with looking at someone else's success and using it to inspire your own? Nothing, if that's what's truly taking place, but most of the time, it means comparing our own everyday bodies and lives to someone else's

(Photoshopped) highlight reels, and then finding our own situation lacking.

One of my particular favorites is the catchphrase "Strong is the new skinny" that's currently sweeping the internet. Taken at face value, this seems like a great motivational truism. No longer do we need to be skinny to be accepted in society! Be strong! Kick ass! Take no prisoners!

Except … every time I've seen this slogan, it is plastered over a picture of an impossibly fit model with unreasonably low body fat. Don't get me wrong–the dedication and effort that it takes to achieve and maintain that type of body is admirable. It's just unrealistic for the vast majority of women (i.e., women whose job description is not "fitness model"). Strong really is the new skinny, because the new standard is just as (or perhaps even more) unattainable as the old. In addition to being impossibly thin, we now need to have rippling muscles and the ability to do a one-handed pushup while rocking a bikini. We're not just fat anymore–we're fat, weak, and uncoordinated. Why even bother? Pass the cupcakes, please.

When we believe we're not worthy, we stop treating ourselves with respect, which includes good nutrition, kind self-talk, regular exercise, and so on. Yes, obesity is fundamentally a result of overeating, but why is everyone eating so much in the first place? There's certainly no lack of information about proper nutrition and portion sizes available to the general population. But in the absence of feeling good about ourselves, external mood enhancers such as food, alcohol, or shopping (to name a few) are a quick fix. Food is particularly easy to abuse in this way, because it's inexpensive, widely available, and socially acceptable. Bad day at work? All it takes is a few quarters in the vending machine to get temporary relief. Unfortunately, the reprieve is short-lived. Shortly after the snack wrappers are in the trash, guilt settles in for a nice long visit. And therein lies our chicken-or-egg dilemma–self-medicating with too much food results in the very thing that triggered the low self-esteem in the first place.

What's a girl to do? A strict diet and exercise plan might take the pounds off, but if your deepest beliefs about yourself are unchanged, it won't be long before you'll find yourself partying with your buddies Ben & Jerry late at night. True change comes from within. Instead of searching outwardly for a reflection of what makes you a person of value–your size, appearance, clothes, or the balance in your bank account–you must start believing you are valuable merely because you exist. That no matter what anyone else thinks, you matter. You are beautiful, fabulous and amazing exactly as you are this very moment.

Of course, that's easier said than done. How can I just change my mind? I've been practicing all of those mean thoughts about myself for years! I'm so good at thinking that way!

This is where running enters the picture. Once upon a time, I was exactly where you are. Running changed all of that, but it didn't happen overnight. I'm hoping that my experiences will help speed up the process for you.

I've been a runner, off and on, for the past fifteen years. I started in the summer of 1998, running laps around my block. At the time, I tipped the scales at 200 pounds, give or take (mostly give), and my block was roughly a half mile around, at least according to the odometer on my '97 Saturn. This was before the era of smart phones and GPS watches, a time when heart rate monitors were just becoming mainstream, and well before cute workout clothes came in anything larger than a size L. I'd never even seen anyone my size running in public! So I ran in too-tight leggings, stretched so thin you could almost see the tattoo on my leg, and covered up my body in men's cotton t-shirts that I picked up for $3 apiece at the local outlet store–shirts so enormous they hung almost to my knees. A cheap digital watch timed my intervals, and more than once I almost fell flat on my face because I was too busy counting down the last five seconds to watch where I was going.

I was slow and couldn't run continuously for more than thirty seconds at a time for those first few weeks. It was difficult and uncomfortable, and most of the time I thought I was going to pass out. More than one person told me I would destroy my knees by running. (Side note: most of the people that describe all the terrible things that will happen to you if you run are not actually runners, which makes them full of crap.

You should ignore them). I worried that my leggings would eventually just split right down the center seam as I catapulted myself across a big puddle, and I wondered if I would ever be able to run a half mile without stopping to walk for part of it. Once, I was chased by a dog and another time was heckled by two little kids that thought the sight of me chugging down the sidewalk was funnier than a fart joke. And on one memorable evening, I stepped out in front of a minivan moments before the driver made an unexpected right turn. She saw me just in time to hit the brakes, but not quickly enough to avoid sending me sprawling on the pavement. Fortunately for both of us, I didn't sustain any serious bodily injuries. My faithful yellow Sony Sports Discman, however, was another story.

I could have used any of these events as excuses not to run, but I felt completely badass when I ran those first laps around the block. Thirty-second intervals turned into 60-second intervals, and pretty soon I was able to run one lap without stopping. I didn't lose a lot of weight through this process–maybe five to ten pounds–but I slowly worked up to running a little more each time. Every milestone reached built up my self-esteem a teeny bit more. I began to tell people I was a runner. It felt incredible.

After a few weeks, I was able to do an entire lap of the block without walking, then two. That fall, I entered a 5K, crossing the finish line in about forty-two minutes. I was nearly dead last, but I finished, and it felt like the sweetest victory of my life. Especially when my best friend's seven-year-old son joined me a few steps before the finish line and crossed with me, his arms waving in the air like we'd just finished a marathon. My self-confidence was at an all-time high. It was a magical experience–and I wanted to hold onto that feeling forever.

The next day, I rested. Then one more day, for good measure. On day three, I'd love to say I laced up my shoes and hit the streets, but I just … didn't. In fact, I didn't run again for a few years. I have no real explanation for why I just stopped doing something that gave me so much joy, other than the mean girl in my head wanted to feel good by eating pizza and ice cream *right this second*, rather than go to all the effort of overcoming the gravity of the couch, changing into unflattering workout clothes, and sweating it out for at least fifteen minutes before the feel-good endorphins kicked in. She also has a lot of opinions, most of which are in the "you'll never be a real runner so why even bother" genre. She's kind of a bitch.

(Spoiler alert: my mean girl is named Whinona. You'll meet her later.)

Fast forward to 2001 and I began commuting a hundred and twenty-five miles, round trip, each day to a desk job. I'm sure you can do the math–an extra two to three hours per day behind the wheel of my car did nothing but increase the size of my ass. Remembering my short-lived glory days as a runner, I joined a gym near my office, and began to run some half-hearted intervals on the treadmill after work. A year later, I sold my house and moved five miles from my employer, to an apartment next to a beautiful bike path along the Schuylkill River. Running was back in my life, and the old magic began to return. I met my future husband, a long-distance runner and triathlete. Jackpot! We hit the trail together every weekend, and after several months, I was able to run a few miles without stopping. The day I managed to run seven miles in a row, I felt like a complete rock star. Nothing was going to stop me this time around!

Buoyed by my success, I signed up to do the 2004 Broad Street Run, a popular local race that stretches ten miles down the very center of Philadelphia. With the race about six months out, and considering that I was already running seventy percent of the distance, it seemed there was plenty of time to train. I set a goal of finishing in two hours or less … and stopped running again.

It wasn't pretty, but I did cross the finish line, and that was my last run for a few years. Inevitably, I began again. Got hooked again. Stopped again. Lather, rinse, repeat.

Fast forward to present day, and I run consistently at least three times a week. Although I'm a bit faster and sleeker than 1998, I'm still a chunky back-of-the-packer, and proud of it! While it is likely that I'll never win any races (unless I'm still running when I'm 70–the field is much thinner at that age), I *always* finish.

You might wonder why I'm qualified to give advice about running, self-esteem, or anything even remotely related to those topics. After fifteen years and hundreds of miles I know a thing or two about both. I also know how to pick myself up, dust myself off and start again. I've been exactly where you are now, and have come through it.

The most important lesson I've learned over the years is that running is a metaphor for success. Take things one step at a time, keep moving forward (even if you have to walk or crawl), and eventually you'll reach your goal. Let go of unrealistic expectations while simultaneously pushing yourself out of your comfort zone. That's the magic formula.

When you think about your workouts this way, the thrill of possibility lies just beyond the next step, even when it sucks. Even in the rain, the snow, or the crushing heat and humidity that passes for summer in Southeastern Pennsylvania. It's all good. It's better than good. It is a high like no other.

It's that moment when you realize you are so freaking *strong* and who gives a fuck about being skinny. When you stop obsessing about whether your butt cheeks are shaking with each step and realize that those glorious glutes are what powers you forward. When you have to double check that your feet are actually touching the ground with each step, because for a moment there it seemed like you might actually be flying. When you find yourself unapologetically weeping at the end of a long run, in awe of your own strength, courage and endurance.

Yeah, that feeling. You can't get that from a cupcake (I've tried).

It doesn't matter how many times you start over, as long as you do. Running will always be there for you, and with it, your self-assurance. You can always begin again. It is never, ever too late. To quote John Bingham, "The miracle isn't that I finished. The miracle is that I had the courage to start."

So be brave, lace up those shoes, and let's get down to business. It's time to run your way back to self-esteem, confidence, and fabulosity.

But first, download and print the Running With Curves Manifesto, and hang it on your bathroom mirror, on the fridge, on the dashboard of your car, or on the back of the front door - for a little extra support when you need it.

www.RunningWithCurves.net/Manifesto

RUNNERS RUN

How do you know you've become a runner? When you realize you own more sneakers than any other type of shoe. When you find yourself discussing the pros and cons of various refueling gels with a straight face. When paying more for compression tights than a designer handbag seems completely normal. I could go on, but the best answer is this:

If you run, you are a runner.

That's it. Fast or slow, short distances or long, twice a month or twice a day, runners run. Whether for thirty miles or thirty seconds, they just run. Regardless of your fitness level, body shape, or weight, you become a runner as soon as you put on your shoes, step out the front door, and run. Voila, you're in the club.

FINDING YOUR BLISS

Everyone that exercises has a reason for pursuing the particular type of workout that appeals to them. For swimmers, it might be the relaxing feel of the water against their skin. For indoor cyclists, the loud music and group atmosphere is energizing. Golfers enjoy the time in nature, or the challenge of competing against themselves. Bullfighters? Well, I'm not really sure why. It all sounds a little crazy to me, but they must get something out of it.

Truly understanding why I choose to run has made it much easier to get out the door on days when I'm busy, tired, or would rather binge-watch TV on Netflix. When I first started, it was strictly an efficient mode of burning calories. Then I realized how great I felt after a run, both physically and mentally, and I started chasing that feeling. Over the years, running has brought a mountain of self-confidence into my life, along with the sweet relief of no longer worrying what anyone else thinks about me. Trust me–once you are free from the burden of others' opinions, the world is your oyster. And the more I run, the more liberated I become.

Most recently, I've realized that I truly love everything about running. And I mean everything: even when it hurts, when the rain is pouring down, or the heat and humidity are so intense that I break a sweat just tying my shoes, I still love it. It's all part of the experience. It is my bliss.

Dictionary.com defines bliss as "supreme happiness; utter joy or contentment", and that pretty much sums up it how it feels to me. That doesn't mean I never get injured, or feel fatigue and frustration. Far from it. Sometimes my body gets so tired I'm not sure how I'm going to take another step (that's when I picture myself as Rocky, running through the streets of South Philly with kids cheering me on. Works like a charm every time).

Bliss co-exists with all of the discomfort and somehow makes it easy to bear. Bliss rocks.

At this point, you're probably rolling your eyes, thinking "Yeah, that's fine for you, but I don't feel bliss – or anything even remotely close–when I run. All I feel is sweaty, tired and frankly, a little pissed off."

Fair enough. I expected some resistance, so I called on my running friends from around the country, women of all shapes, sizes, lifestyles and fitness levels, to share the reasons they run:

"My favorite part about running is those moments, and they do happen, when you are in such a rhythm that it seems the world is moving by you instead of you running through it. It's an amazing feeling. I love being in the groove of running. I love how it benefits my physical and emotional health. I love the opportunity it gives me to be in nature just thinking, processing and pondering without interruption. I love the conversations you can have with a good running buddy. I love being reminded that I *can* do *anything*."
  – McKenzie D., Bend, OR

"Once I started running consistently, I fell in love with it. There IS such a thing as a runner's high. Not only do you feel a great sense of accomplishment after finishing a run or reaching a new goal, but there is also something that happens chemically inside me when I run consistently. Sometimes, I just want to drop what I am doing and run...even when I am nicely dressed and on my way into work, my body says *run*. Having a spontaneous urge to do something healthy is such a great feeling."

    – Abby S., Westchester, PA

"It means I've accomplished a personal goal. It means that I get to be proud of myself. And it means that I get to face the voice inside that tells me to take it easy and tell it to be quiet while I put on my shoes, head out the door, and go move my body. The resulting sense of pride and accomplishment is why I do it."

    – Gina D., Santa Rosa, CA

"Running does make me feel happier and more fit, which helps me feel better about myself and more confident. Again, since we're being honest here, when I feel confident I'm more likely to seduce my husband, take risks at work, speak in public … it's a good cycle."

    – Amanda R., Wayne, PA

Each of these women has found her own personal running nirvana–she knows exactly what she's getting from the experience and it's more than just burning calories or losing weight. It's confidence, and it keeps her coming back again and again.

My advice to you is to really understand why you run, or why you *want* to run. Make a list, and keep adding to it over time. Review it on those days when you think there are too many other things you'd rather do than run, or when it seems like the world is conspiring against you. It's OK if you don't know all the answers right now, all you need to do is give it some thought.

Some days it will be tough to find your happy place while running, especially in the beginning. This is to be expected. Even if you know exactly why you're out there pounding the pavement, the future payoff might not feel worth the effort of the present moment. Keep going anyway, and focus on what *is* going well. It might be the simple fact that you got your butt out the door at 6am when you wanted to sleep for another half-hour, or that your shins don't hurt quite as much as last time. Whatever it is, find it, grab it, and celebrate it.

Just do me a favor–don't ever use running as a reason to beat yourself up for being inadequate. If your workout just didn't go as planned, focusing on what *did* go well is a hell of a lot less painful than being pissed off because you didn't set a personal record. You can deconstruct why things went south, and use that information to learn and improve, but please don't use it as evidence of failure. There is no such thing as a bad run, only the one you didn't do.

TAKING THE FIRST STEP

Martin Luther King, Jr. once said "You don't have to see the whole staircase. Just take the first step."

Wise words.

But even taking that first step can be daunting, particularly if you're brand new to the sport. The human mind can be quite contradictory: wanting to try something that we believe will be rewarding, while simultaneously reminding us that we're likely to fail, so why even bother?

Many women believe they are not well-suited to running, based on the simple fact that when they do, they can't run very far. Often this is just due to a lack of conditioning, or trying to go too fast, too soon. Running is hard work, and it takes awhile for your body–especially your heart, lungs, and legs–to adapt to the challenge. Just because you can't run for 20 minutes your first time out doesn't mean you're not meant to be a runner, it just means you've got work to do.

Consistency is critical to improvement, and one of the easiest ways to ensure that you're keeping up with your workouts is to follow a training schedule. For example, if your goal is to run three miles, you might choose a training plan with three runs per week, each week gradually increasing time, distance, and/or speed until you achieve your goal. But looking at your desired end state vs. your current fitness level can be a bit overwhelming. And what do most of us do when faced with a seemingly insurmountable challenge? Panic, hit the snooze button, and vow to start tomorrow. Repeat for two months. Chastise yourself when you realize you are no closer to your goal.

I've got a better idea: just envision the very first step of the staircase. Instead of freaking out about how far you are from your goal, concern yourself with what you need to do today, or even the next ten minutes. That might be as simple as putting your shoes on and going outside, or driving to the gym. Then worry about the next step. Gina D. sums it up perfectly:

"What I love more than anything else about running is the lesson it teaches me to take life in small steps and to focus on the moment. I liken the experience to knitting. You can only knit a project one stitch at a time, so you better learn to enjoy each stitch, otherwise you'll get to the end of the project and will have hated doing it the entire time. When I run and look way ahead at how far I have to go, it can become overwhelming, so I focus on just one step in front of me and stop looking at the overall distance. It takes me further that way."

My husband once asked me if I could see improvement in my performance from week to week. I thought about it for a moment, and answered "No." Unless you are an absolute beginner, a week is really too short of time to see measurable changes. But if I look back at where I was three months, six months or two years ago, the improvement is immediately visible. It feels great to see that difference, and realize how far I've come. If I'd spent every week of the past two years looking for evidence of change, however, I would have been sorely disappointed.

Placing too much importance on seeing progression can be a huge de-motivator. Just ask any woman who has been desperately trying to lose weight, only to see a big goose-egg on the scale week after week–if her only reason for making healthy choices every day is to see the number on the scale decrease, you can bet she'll be face-down in a pan of lasagna before too long. The same goes for running. If your final result is more important to you than the reason you're on the journey in the first place, you're likely to quit and head right back to your favorite spot on the couch.

This isn't to say that setting goals, such as a future race, is a bad idea. Quite the opposite, as this can help you focus your efforts. But you shouldn't rely solely on an endpoint to keep you going.

When your primary reason for running is to build your self-esteem with every step, that's really all the motivation you need to start moving. Consider each and every step a stitch in your scarf of self-confidence, and start knitting.

GETTING STARTED

Now that I've convinced you that running is a wonder drug, able to solve all your problems and give you the confidence you've always wanted, what next?

Duh, it's time to run.

Cue the deluge of questions: Where should I run? When? How far? What happens when I get tired? Won't I get injured because I'm overweight? Should I sign up for a race? Where do I get cute running clothes that fit? Do I need a GPS watch? What the heck are compression tights? Why is running so *hard*?

Patience, grasshopper. All in good time.

Our first goal is to get you running consistently–because once you've got a few runs under your belt, you've built evidence that you are indeed a runner. And what do runners do? All together now … *they run*! When you believe you're a runner, you are much more likely to get out there and do it. Which builds more evidence. It's the opposite of a vicious cycle–more like a self-confidence spiral, perhaps? Yes, that's what we'll call it. Imagine that each and every run you complete is a magical step in the spiral staircase to the glistening ivory tower of self-esteem.

Gag.

But seriously, consistency not only gets physical results like running faster and farther, it builds up your positive belief system. And the stronger those good feelings are, the more likely you are to keep running. So without further ado, let's begin.

Download this 1-week jumpstart plan and have it handy as you go through the next few sections so you can take notes and be ready to start off with confidence:
www.RunningWithCurves.net/Jumpstart

DECISIONS, DECISIONS

The first question to tackle is where and when you should run. The short answer? Wherever and whenever you'll be most likely to actually do it. This means that if you love being outdoors in all four seasons, you might want to rethink putting that $5000 treadmill on layaway. But if you don't mind working out in your basement and have all six seasons of Breaking Bad on BluRay, a treadmill might be the right choice. Either way, I urge you to experiment a lot in the beginning to find what works for you. Run on your local roads or trails, at the gym, after you get up in the morning, and during your lunch break to see what you like best. There are pros and cons to every scenario, but the most important thing is that it is right for *you*.

CLIMATE CONTROLLED COMFORT OR THE GREAT OUTDOORS?

Ah, the great debate. Is it better to run on a treadmill, or brave the elements and head outside? A lot depends on your work and family schedules, where you live and, of course, personal preference. Most likely, no single option will be perfect – rather, you will find that a combination of places works best for you.

Let's consider the gym. Pros: convenience, quality of equipment, air-conditioning, and safety. In this day and age, many of us have a gym strategically located close to either work or home. Gyms usually have high-quality treadmills built for heavy use, which means they won't shake and shimmy when you push the speed past 3.5 mph. With a more cushioned surface than pavement or cement, the impact to your joints is lower. Another bonus of the treadmill is the incline, allowing you to run uphill when you want to. Most facilities even have TVs hanging from the ceiling (although in my experience, someone else is always in control of the remote, and they always want to watch golf). Gyms have locker rooms, which means you can shower right afterwards if you choose, as well as lock up your stuff while you're running. There is also the luxury of air-conditioning in the summer, heat in the winter, and a roof when it is raining. Unlike roads, treadmills are traffic-free, so you can crank up the tunes as loud as you want without fear of getting run over by someone texting and driving. Working out around other people that are also sweating, huffing and puffing can be motivational, and the hidden benefit here is that you can secretly race the person on the next machine (something I highly recommend).

Cons? Not too many, aside from cost and hygiene. Most gyms are not free. However, in recent years, low cost gyms have been popping up all over the place. If you're not looking for a space with lots of bells and whistles, you can probably get a membership someplace for less than $20 a month and no annual contract. So cost shouldn't be too much of a barrier. The questionable cleanliness of a public gym is the biggest drawback, in my opinion. Sure, *you* wipe down your equipment with disinfectant after use, and wash your hands after you leave the bathroom, *but not everyone does.* The residue of others' bodily fluids are on nearly every surface at a gym–the whole point of being there is to generate sweat–and you will eventually (and probably unknowingly) come into contact with someone else's bacterial and viral leftovers. Icky, yes. Also inevitable. So do your best not to put your hands in your mouth while you're there and make sure to shower pretty quickly after you're done. And if you're sick, stay home. Nobody else wants your germs.

If you prefer treadmill running, but don't want a full gym membership, consider getting a treadmill for your home. This is the ultimate in convenience, because unless the power goes out, you're guaranteed to be able to run. Actually, you can still get a workout even if there's no power–it takes a lot of strength to push the belt without electrical assistance, but it can be done. Truth be told, it feels just like pushing a manual lawnmower up a steep hill, and that's a pretty awesome workout. A home treadmill session is also a great opportunity to catch up on your favorite movies or TV shows, and you don't have to fight anyone for the remote. Win-win!

Other than the boredom factor and up-front investment cost, there aren't too many cons about treadmills aside from one: running on a belt does not challenge your body the way running outdoors does, because the belt is doing some of the work for you by pulling your feet backwards. And if you're training for a race, this could be an issue. There is no wind resistance or terrain variability on a treadmill either, which is always a factor outside. To compensate, consider varying the incline and speed to better mimic outdoor conditions, if your goal is to complete a 5K or other event.

So that's the scoop on the indoors–now let's talk about what's outside the gym. Running outdoors has advantages and disadvantages too, but unlike your trusty treadmill, there are many more options. Unless you live in a tree house in the rainforest, outdoor running is a convenient option. Step out the front door and you're ready to roll. If your neighborhood is replete with sidewalks and well-manicured lawns, consider yourself lucky. You are in running heaven. Also, please consider inviting me over to be your running buddy. I'll bring my famous homemade granola bars.

Those of you that don't have miles of traffic-free streets and sidewalks just outside your front door need not fret, however, you'll just need to be a bit more careful: look both ways before crossing the street, be aware of approaching traffic, follow the rules of the road and watch for potholes or other obstacles. Whatever your road situation, pounding the pavement can be a tremendously joyous way to get your run on. Whether in the city, the country, or somewhere in between, running outside means you have a constantly changing landscape to watch, and although you will have to go uphill from time to time, that means you also get to enjoy the delights of going downhill. Since we live in such a traffic-centered society, roads are everywhere (sidewalks, not so much), thus there are infinite possibilities to wear out even the most tireless runner. And with all of the free online mapping tools available, you can plan out your route in detail ahead of time–or just throw caution to the wind and see where your feet take you.

The downsides to street and sidewalk running are few, but do need to be considered. The shoulders of most roads are sloped to allow for water runoff. This means that you'll constantly be running at a very slight angle which over time can result in muscle imbalances. To counteract this, make sure you don't do every run on this type of surface. Mix it up with sidewalks, trails and track running if possible. Traffic is also a big concern, and although rural roads tend to have fewer cars, this also means those vehicles that are on the road will be driving faster and probably not paying as close attention to the side of the road as might someone that is in heavier traffic. Always run facing oncoming traffic and stay aware. Be ready to duck and roll into a ditch if necessary. Wear appropriate reflective gear and brightly colored clothing at all times, but especially at dusk and after dark. Headlamps and blinking lights may look dorky, but if you want to run after sundown, they can be invaluable. It could mean the difference between a successful run or a ride to the hospital.

Pavement and cement can pose tripping hazards due to the potential for holes, cracks and uneven surfaces (especially if you live in Pennsylvania where the unofficial state flag is orange and says "Caution, Men Working"). Roads and sidewalks are also harder on the joints. Again, watch where you're going and make sure to mix up your surfaces and you should be fine.

The final challenge with running outdoors is the weather, and this is the one that most people complain about. Cold, heat, humidity and precipitation pose their own challenges, but unless there is lightning or hail (or the temp is below zero degrees Fahrenheit), there's no reason you can't suit up accordingly and soldier on.

By the way, running any given route in the rain makes you feel 50% more hardcore than running the very same route on a sunny day–which puts you several levels higher up the self-esteem spiral by default. Now that's something to consider!

Finally, let's talk track and trail. Tracks are awesome–no traffic, outside, and a nice cushy running surface. If you can find a nearby high school or college that will let you run on their track when the students aren't using it, you've got a fabulous training tool available to you. Bonus points if you can find one that is well-lit after dark! The only drawback to a track workout is the lack of hills (of course, to some this might be their best feature), and the fact that sometimes there are football games, track meets, or other activities going on that will take precedence over your need to run.

Trail running is incredible, but also much more demanding physically, due to the elastic nature of the ground. Ditto for running on grass. I won't go into the physics of it all, but the more "give" your running surface has, the harder your muscles have to work to keep you moving. This is a good thing overall because running on pavement will feel easy after you've trained on packed dirt or grass, but you'll definitely run slower in the woods. Watch for tree roots, gopher holes and small animals, and make sure you don't get poked in the eye by a stray branch. If at all possible, bring a map and tuck it into your pocket or a backpack. It's easy to ask for directions when you're lost in an unfamiliar neighborhood, but there usually aren't too many pedestrians in the woods at your local state park. GPS is your friend; use it if you have it. Finally, for a true trail run, you'll need sturdier shoes, or at the very least a pair that you don't mind getting dirty.

THE BEST TIME TO RUN

Alrighty! Now that we've covered the where, what about the when? The best timing for your runs can be a bit trickier to nail down. It mainly depends on your schedule and whether you're a night owl or an early bird. If you're willing and able to get up an hour earlier, morning runs are a great way to make sure you fit it in as well as start your day off right. I'm not going to lie to you and say that running first thing is easy-peasy, but there are a few things you can do make the process less painful. Remove as many obstacles from your path as possible (or to look at it another way, create obstacles to staying in bed):

- Lay out your clothes the night before (or pack your gym bag and *put it in the car*).

- Put your alarm clock on the other side of the room so you actually have to get out of bed to turn it off.

- Go to bed a little early to make sure you're well-rested.

- Train your spouse to push you out of bed when the alarm goes off.

- If you have a running buddy, make a date so you know someone will be waiting for you–this works particularly well if said running buddy has no issues with publicly shaming you for not showing up.

- Make sure your phone, MP3 player or other devices are fully charged (or charging) before you go to bed.

- Keep your list of reasons why you run on your phone or in your nightstand, and review it if you want to sleep in.

- And my favorite trick of all, just get dressed. When the alarm goes off, tell yourself all you need to do is put on your workout clothes and shoes. Once that's done, tackle the next step.

If evening workouts are better for you, the same principles apply. Remove the barriers and excuses ahead of time:

- Pack your gym bag the night before and put it in the car.
- Keep a spare set of everything (clothes, sports bra, ponytail holder, sneakers, socks, even headphones) in your car.
- Run at work if possible, or choose a gym or trail that is on your way home.
- If you run in your neighborhood, get dressed to run at work–when you get home, don't even go in the house, just hop out of the car and start running.
- Make sure you have a small pre-run snack available to eat in the afternoon.
- Listen to energizing music in the car on the way home from work to get yourself pumped up.
- Plan to meet a buddy for your run.

If you have a flexible work schedule, try running at lunch or another time during the day. And if you're a stay-at-home mom with little ones, running strollers have come a long way–taking your child with you on your workout makes him happy too!

"I have an eleven-month-old son, so I have to take him with me most days. Getting my son outside and on the road motivates me to get out the door. He is a much happier little guy after a stroll. I have to work around nap times and make sure I take loops that keep me close to the house just in case he gets fussy. I think getting him moving and exposed to the fresh air is great for him, too."
    –Nina G., Cherry Hill, NJ

The bottom line is, the only perfect time to run is the one that works for you. Consider your schedule, lifestyle, and personality and try out a few things. You'll need to experiment to find the best fit, but eventually you'll figure it out.

DEALING WITH THE WEATHER

Running on a treadmill has one distinct advantage over outdoor running: the climate indoors is usually a cool seventy degrees, with 0% chance of precipitation. If only the rest of the world was like that! But it isn't, and sooner or later you'll need to figure out how to deal with Mother Nature.

The height of summer is my least favorite time to run. I'm not a fan of the heat, so when the temperature and humidity get so high I wonder if I've been teleported to a rainforest, my first instinct is to turn up the air conditioning, lie on the couch and crack open a cold beer. With a little planning, however, running in the heat doesn't need to be a suffer-fest. Keep the following advice in mind and you'll be fine:

- Run early in the morning or late in the evening, when the temperatures are lower.
- Slow down. Heat and humidity are hard on your body. The more moisture in the air, the slower your sweat will

evaporate. This means that you're much more prone to overheating–to avoid this, you'll need to ease up a bit on your pace and take some extra walk breaks. If you normally cover a mile in twelve minutes when the temperature is sixty degrees and dry, you might only manage a fourteen-minute mile on a humid, eighty degree day. This is normal, and doesn't mean you're getting slower.

- Expose yourself. The more skin you have uncovered, the easier it will be to keep cool. This means sleeveless tops, and tights that don't go past your knees.

- Wear a lightweight headband or a visor to keep sweat out of your eyes. Avoid hats, which trap heat.

- Don't apply sunscreen above your eyebrows. If you do this, you'll end up with sunscreen in your eyes, guaranteed.

- Drink water. Carrying a bottle with you while you run can be a hassle, so leave it next to a fencepost or tree that you'll pass by more than once on your route. If my stash-spot is in a high-traffic area, I usually tape a note to my bottle that says "Please don't take me. My owner is out running right now and is really looking forward to drinking me later!"

- Put ice cubes in your bra at the start of your run. I'm serious.
- If you find yourself overheating, dump water over your head. This is a really fast way to cool down.
- And finally, know the warning signs of heatstroke: chills, dizziness, muscle cramps, weakness and nausea. Always carry your phone in case you need to call for help.

Winter running is also a challenge, but still completely possible. Again, it's all about heat management. You might start out with your teeth chattering but after a few minutes of running your body temperature rises and suddenly that long-sleeved shirt and fleece jacket feel like a neoprene wetsuit. To avoid this scenario, dress yourself in light layers–especially on top–so that you can peel them off as your body warms up. One strategy I like to use is to leave my house with a jacket, run for five minutes or so until I'm warmed up, then swing back by my house and drop the jacket off in the mailbox. Don't forget about water, either. Dry, winter air causes your sweat to evaporate quickly, which means you'll need to replenish your fluids often.

No matter the season, you'll always have to deal with some sort of precipitation. There's really no reason not to run in the rain or snow (unless there's lightning, hail, or flash flooding in the area), but it can be uncomfortable if you're not prepared. You won't find too many waterproof running jackets on the market, because if it keeps water off your body, it also traps any moisture you generate - which leads to chafing. So if you choose to run in the rain or snow (personally, I love it), plan on getting wet. Use extra BodyGlide on your feet and other body parts prone to chafing, and make sure to put your electronics in a water-proof case (or a Ziploc baggie). Keep an extra close eye on traffic, too–wet or icy roads can be slippery so stick to routes where you'll be far from moving vehicles.

EXPECT THE UNEXPECTED

Even the best-laid plans can fall apart sometimes, so it's important to have a backup strategy. If you're a die-hard trail runner, where will you run when the spring floods wash out your favorite path? What if you get to the gym and all the treadmills are taken? Will you run outdoors during your favorite seasons and indoors the rest of the year? What if, despite your best efforts, you sleep through your alarm? You'll need to determine how you will manage through those (inevitable) times when your preferred running option is unavailable. Otherwise, you might find yourself stomping around the house in frustration, wondering how many times you'd have to run up and down the stairs to cover one mile.

For the record, one mile of stairs equals 528 trips up and 528 trips back down, based on a standard staircase with 15 steps. I don't even know how long that would take, and I'd rather run an entire marathon, on a treadmill, in total silence, in a dark room, than find out.

My point is, if you fail to plan, you plan to fail. Think ahead, remove as many obstacles as possible, and you'll rarely miss a workout due to unforeseen circumstances. The more workouts you finish, the higher you climb on your self-esteem spiral.

YOUR INNER MEAN GIRL

When you first start running, you will experience all manner of new sensations in your body. In particular, your legs, feet, knees, hips, back, lungs … almost everywhere. Including your brain! Training your mind to run is just as tough (perhaps even more so) than your body, regardless of your weight or fitness level.

Many of these new feelings will be uncomfortable, perhaps even painful. As I've said before, running is hard work, and it takes time to adapt. So you might be tempted to interpret these phenomena as a warning sign from your body that it is time to take a rest break. With a Snickers bar.

In a nutshell, your body is a lot like Congress. When the going gets tough, there is often a lot of hand-waving, pounding of fists, and threats of a government shutdown. But with a little coaxing and negotiating, eventually everyone settles down and things continue operating as normal (although I'd venture to say your body is far more efficient than the US government).

The trick is to learn the difference between actual pain, which should be respected and tended, and your inner mean girl, who is just trying to convince you that you suck. Yeah, she's a bully. She's also relentless, unless you learn how to handle her.

When I'm running and a thought like "I want to stop" pops into my head, I use a body-scanning technique to figure out what to do. Fortunately, the body scan can be done while running, and doesn't require any special equipment. Starting with my toes and slowly working my way upwards … feet, heels, calves, shins, knees, thighs, hips, spine, chest, back, shoulders, neck … to the very top of my head, I look for actual pain, such as a sharp, stabbing feeling, anything that feels like pulling, popping or tearing (tearing is always bad), or a deep ache that appears to be getting worse. These are usually signs that something is amiss, and running through these signals can lead to injury.

When you feel the urge to stop due to potential pain, you'll need to hone right in on the sensations to see if the pain is real or imaginary. Often when you focus all your attention on the body part in question, the feeling disappears. This is how you know your mean girl is up to her old shenanigans.

Of course, if you detect true pain, please stop (or at least slow down), assess, and take appropriate action. If what you're feeling is general fatigue, weariness, boredom, or disappears when you focus on it, you might be a victim of mean girl mischief. This is great news for you, because I'm going to teach you how to kick her to the curb so you can keep going.

It will help enormously if you can give your mean girl a name. Trust me, this will make conversations with her much easier. And you will need to talk to her, or rather *stand up to her*. She's just a playground bully and when you hold your ground, she'll back down, I promise.

As I mentioned earlier, I call my mean girl Whinona. This is because she whines a *lot*, and her voice in my head is high pitched, nasal, and piercing. Also, because I don't personally know anyone called Winona, I felt comfortable that I wouldn't insult any of my friends or family by appropriating that name. But if your mean girl reminds you of your ninth grade frenemy, or your mother-in-law, feel free to use that name! It will be our little secret.

Sometimes Whinona starts in on me before I've even put my shoes on:

"You worked really hard yesterday. You need to rest."

"Let's just wait to see what kind of wine Hoda & Kathie Lee are drinking on the Today Show. Then we'll go."

"All of your workout clothes are in the laundry."

And my personal favorite:

"Nap first. Run later."

This one is always a lie. What she really means is "Nap first, cookie later, then we'll play Solitaire on the iPad."

The best defense is a good offense, and after years of practice, I'm now fully prepared with an arsenal of short & sweet rebuttals. Here's an example of a recent conversation:

This is hard. (You're right. Keep moving.)

I don't want to. (Your opinion is noted. Keep moving.)

You're running too slow. (So what? Keep moving.)

My legs are tired. (Awesome! That means we're working hard! Keep moving.)

That woman is staring at you (Must be because I'm so awesome. Keep moving.)

This hurts. (So does being out of shape. Keep moving.)

My toe hurts. (Let me check...sorry, it's not that bad. Keep moving.)

I'm bored. (Really? This is a great time to meditate, write a blog post in your head, see if you can remember all fifty states, work on your breathing, plan a vacation, look at the landscaping in your neighborhood for ideas …)

You look ridiculous–sweaty, red-faced, and panting like a porn star. (Well duh, that's what people look like when they run.)

You're too fat to run. (Really? Because I am running.)

I'm tired. (Me too–tired of hearing you whine. Shut up so I can finish this run.)

You get the picture. Arguing with her always makes things worse–the key is to listen to her complaints and acknowledge them, then respond calmly, logically, without getting emotional, and definitely without allowing further discussion on the topic.

A word of warning: she will almost certainly try to convince you that it is much harder to run if you're overweight, and that you might injure yourself. While she has a fair point, in my opinion she is playing to your emotions. An overweight woman has more body mass to move than someone that weighs less, that much is true. She also has correspondingly stronger legs from moving that very same weight around day in and day out, which somewhat compensates for the extra load. Regardless, it will take more effort and probably a longer training program for a woman that weighs 250 pounds to be able to run a twelve-minute mile than one who is starting at 150 pounds. But that's where it ends. All new runners, regardless of size or fitness level have the same mental hurdles to overcome and the same mean girl to vanquish, which really equalizes the playing field. If you work at your current ability, heed the warning signs of injury, and keep a consistent schedule, you'll get stronger. It doesn't matter if it takes you two months or two years, because if you stay focused on the reasons you run (which hopefully include building up your self-esteem), it won't matter how long it takes, all it will matter is that you keep doing it.

Working through the physical and mental discomfort of running can actually be rewarding, despite what your version of Whinona might tell you. Pain is inevitable, but suffering is optional. Listening to your mean girl is suffering. Don't give her the satisfaction.

NOW WHAT?

Now that you've figured out where and when to run, and how to shut down your inner mean girl like a boss, you're probably wondering how far and fast you should run. That is, of course, a great question, but since there are hundreds of books, websites and apps out there to tell you how to do just that, I'm not going to explore that topic in too much detail here. The purpose of this book is to show you that you can become a runner in the body you have right now–and to help you build self-esteem along the way.

That being said, I do have a few words to say on the topic. The kindest thing you can do for yourself is to start off slowly, by running intervals at a pace that feels difficult, but not impossible. Depending on your current fitness level, this might mean you start with a thirty-minute workout, where you run for fifteen seconds and walk for sixty, or it might mean you run for two minutes and walk for thirty seconds to recover. It doesn't matter where you start, just that you keep at it and test your boundaries a bit during each workout. Running is hard work. If it feels easy, you're probably not pushing hard enough. Conversely, if you spend your entire workout feeling like you're about to see your breakfast again, you might be going too hard. Aim to spend a decent chunk of your running time in the sweet spot between effort and ease. It takes practice, but with time you'll get there. Using the body scan technique I described earlier will help you with that.

Whichever training plan you choose, just remember that everyone's body is different, and while these plans are created for the average person, they don't necessarily take *your* individual needs into account. If you are having trouble progressing to the next week in your training schedule, this doesn't mean you are a failure! It just means you need to adapt the plan to meet your needs.

The most important thing is to stick with it, go at your own pace, and be insanely proud of everything you complete.

THE NEXT PHASE

You've accomplished quite a bit so far: settling into a comfortable routine and creating backup plans for your backup plans. All that's left to do is run your butt off and watch yourself get faster and faster each week, right?

Oops. About that … I've got some bad news.

There's no doubt that a running program is new and exciting at the start, when each week brings measurable improvement, and you can barely wait for the next workout to find out what your body can do. The awesome thing about this phase is that rapid gains in speed, distance or duration keep you thirsty for more, and build up your self-esteem tremendously. Each workout is an opportunity to push yourself just a little farther, and you'll often find that you exceed your own expectations. This is the honeymoon phase of running and it feels spectacular. Visions of entering a marathon dance in your head, and you realize that you are, in fact, a bona fide superhero. With a cape, and possibly even an invisible plane.

Beginners tend see results faster than experienced runners, because they're starting, well, right at the beginning. During your first week as a runner, you might run thirty second intervals interspersed with ninety seconds of walking, but after a few workouts, you'll realize you can double that time to a full minute–a 100% increase in performance. A week or two later you're running two or three minutes at a time, doubling your endurance yet again. Fast forward three months, and you're consistently running for twenty minutes at time. Amazing! Your days of running thirty second intervals are a distant memory, but the delight of doubling your running time in a matter of days is still fresh in your mind.

Now that you're conquering longer runs with ease, adding a minute or two to the length of your runs seems insignificant. Ramping up from twenty to twenty-two minutes is a 10% improvement, which is great return on investment if you're saving for retirement, but doesn't seem quite so glamorous to a brand new runner, who is used to 100% gains every few weeks. You should know, however, that 10% is a *huge* improvement in the world of elite runners, and can mean the difference between taking home the gold or not getting a medal. It's all about perspective.

Regardless, once the honeymoon is over, you'll need to look at the big picture, rather than a weekly snapshot, to see a noticeable change. We've talked at length about finding the underlying reasons you run, and keeping them in mind on those days when you want to roll over and go back to sleep. But it also helps to cultivate a few extra reasons–such as short or long-term goals, or an accountability partner, to get you through the tough times.

There are any number of ways to keep yourself interested and your routine feeling fresh and new– the only limit is your imagination. Consider your personality, fitness goals, and lifestyle: Are you someone that likes delayed gratification, or do you prefer immediate rewards? Do you like to count down the days to an event, or let your rewards build up over time? Do you crave group interaction, or are you a lone wolf?

Instant gratification junkies are motivated by a quick hit of success. The trick is to choose something that is easily achievable in the near future so it holds your interest. For example, if you're able to run a half-mile now, strive to run a mile without stopping (then two, then three, etc). If you can run a mile in fourteen minutes, work towards running it in thirteen minutes. You get the picture.

Other ideas:

- Begin adding 0.5 mph to your regular treadmill speed for one interval, then build up to running all your intervals at the new speed.

- Make it up that really tough hill on your regular route without stopping to rest.
- Pick a nearby destination and work up to running there from your house.
- Find someone running ahead of you and catch up to them.
- On a track, see how fast you can complete one lap, then try to beat your time.

If you savor the process of achieving a goal more than the goal itself, choose something that is farther in the future, such as a race. Or get creative:

- Work towards accumulating distance over time, such as 100 miles in three months
- Get a wall map of your state, plot a course to run from edge to edge, and track your progress on the map. (If you live in Rhode Island, this might be more of a short-term goal.)
- Put $1 in a jar after every run and work towards a specific savings target. Reward

yourself with something fun like a massage or a cute running outfit when you hit it. Or treat me with something fun! It's always better to give than receive, right?

- Pick a race and train for it (more about that later).

- Keep a journal describing each run, however you see fit. Include your distance, time, weather, how you felt, what you thought about, things you saw along the route–whatever is meaningful to you.

- Set up a series of mini-goals that take you incrementally towards a bigger achievement.

- Chart your progress using a spreadsheet or a big wall chart. This helps you visualize just how much you've accomplished (and it's just plain fun, for Post-it Note nerds like me).

Of course, not everybody is concerned with going faster or farther. If you couldn't care less about your running stats and just want to spice things up a bit, here are some ideas that are focused more on fun than progress:

- Try a new route each week.
- Mix up your running playlist.
- Wear a tutu to your next race (I'm only partly joking–this is an actual thing. Google it.)
- Break up the monotony by incorporating strength training into your runs: stop for body-weight or resistance band exercises in between running intervals.
- Literally run errands. Run to the library, post office, drug store. Save gas and get your workout in! Just don't buy eggs. It's no fun to run home with eggs in your backpack.
- High-five everyone you pass.
- Run backwards for short distances (but only if you're in a safe area, like a track).
- Incorporate thirty-second intervals of skipping–fun, silly and challenging.

Another sure-fire way to keep the mojo alive is to get pumped up with music. Getting lost in the beat can make the minutes and miles fly by.

The best songs inspire me to pick up my pace, keep going a little longer, or power up a tough hill when I'd rather walk. Dance, hip hop and techno tunes seem to work best for me, but whatever music gets your toes tapping will do the job. One trick I use is to reserve my favorite songs for my runs, and refrain from listening to them at other times–this makes me excited to put on my sneakers, because I know the dance party in my head is about to start. If you're a treadmill runner, try this same strategy with your favorite TV shows or movies. Avid reader? Load up your MP3 player with an audiobook.

Just don't read on the treadmill. It's almost impossible to run and read, and you might find yourself tripping and flying off the back of the machine if you try. Entertainment for everyone else, but pretty painful for you. So save the books and magazines for an easy day on the recumbent bike, unless you want to end up in a YouTube video of exercise fails.

YOU'VE GOT A FRIEND

Running can be a great opportunity to spend time with friends or meet new people, and can help you stay motivated. Whether you're on a trail or side-by-side treadmills at the gym, running with a buddy has a million advantages (well, maybe not a million, but definitely a lot):

- Bonding: Catch up on each other's lives (and all the juicy gossip) without the extra calories of a margarita or a triple-foam latte.
- Accountability: Knowing someone is counting on you to be there for a workout (and that they'll be pretty pissed off if you don't show up) is a pretty strong motivator.
- Encouragement: Having someone to commiserate with when the going gets tough can mean the difference between quitting halfway through or finishing strong.

And it's just plain fun to run with someone else!

For outdoor runs, try to choose a partner that runs at a similar ability, and lay out the ground rules ahead of time–choose a pace, distance and interval schedule that allows each of you to get the workout you need. It might be a slow day for one of you and a fast day for the other, or perhaps you'll do the first half of the run together and finish separately.

A few words of warning about the buddy plan: running (and exercise in general) can decrease your inhibitions, and sometimes there is a tendency to, how shall I say this, *overshare* after you're all warmed up and have run out of gossip. Sure, finding out that your bestie leads a double-life as a stripper will keep you running for a few extra miles, but she needs to know that her secret is safe with you. Don't break the code. Whatever happens on the run, stays on the run.

If you prefer a group environment, check out your local running stores–they often have free groups that run after work or on weekend mornings. Before you show up for your first run, however, be sure to ask the right questions of the organizer. The website might say that all levels are welcome, but if their idea of a beginning runner is a twelve-minute-per-mile pace and you're running much slower than that, you're going to set yourself up to feel pretty bad when the group takes off and you end up running by yourself for most of the workout. Find out who leads the runs, what the general pace is, if there's anyone designated to stay behind and keep track of stragglers. It also helps to understand what the route will be like. Will you be running on sidewalks, trails, or high traffic areas? Is the terrain flat or hilly? How many miles are covered in a typical outing? Are there options to do a shorter loop? What happens if you get lost?

If you can't find a group that meets your needs at your local running store, check out Meetup.com or a similar site to find people at your ability, or consider a virtual running club.

Psst - the best free running group on the internet is the Running With Curves Virtual Running Club on Facebook, with hundreds of women exactly like you
Join here:
RunningWithCurves.net/jointhecommunity

In addition to running clubs, the popularity of running courses is on the rise. These groups typically run for six or eight weeks, and are designed to guide people with no running experience through a training program culminating in a race. Experts are available to help you with proper form, advise on training plans, and ensure that nobody gets left behind.

Just because the honeymoon is over doesn't mean the fun has to stop. Finding ways to keep the love alive ensures that you'll have a long, happy relationship with your new sport.

And if, despite all of the above, you find yourself taking a few months (or even years) off from running, don't despair! It took me 15 years to make my running habit stick. You can always start up again. That's the beautiful thing about running–it will always be there for you, waiting patiently for your return.

"I read a "Marathons for Dummies" book several years ago. It claimed that there was no such thing as "jogging." If you are not walking then you are running. That stuck with me. I am not a fast runner, but I am a runner. I often tell people, "I may not have speed but I have endurance." There are periods when I run every day, periods when I run a couple of times a week, and even sometimes when I don't run at all, but I am still a runner."

-McKenzie D., Bend, Oregon

RUNNERS GONNA RUN

Everyone has that person in their life that feels the need to rain on your parade. Actually, you're pretty fortunate if it's *only* one person. They're basically your inner mean girl come to life - dropping comments designed to make you feel worse and themselves feel superior. These people are rarely runners–we're a pretty positive and supportive bunch, and we love new recruits–but they might have tried to become a runner in the past and failed. Regardless, your success and joy with your new sport makes them feel worse about themselves, so they'll try to discourage you from pursuing your dream:

"You're going to destroy your knees."

"Real runners don't take walk breaks."

"You're just a jogger, not a runner."

"Running is dangerous–I heard about a guy who had a heart attack while doing a marathon last year!"

"Don't you get bored? Running is just so boring!"

Yeah, yeah, yeah. Everyone has an opinion, and they're entitled to speak it. But the only way someone else's opinions can hurt you is if you believe them–so don't! Recognize their words for what they are–a reflection on the speaker, not you. The easiest way to deal with this type of person is to simply say "thanks for your concern," and change the subject. Haters gonna hate. It's human nature. Fortunately, runners gonna run.

Once you've learned how to deal with the external haters, you might find that your mean girl has a few more tricks up her sleeve. Whinona loves to compare me to others, and in the absence of that, to myself.

Looking at how fast, far, or frequently someone else runs, how much weight she's lost from running, how much cuter her outfit is than yours–basically anything that leaves you feeling "*less than*" in any way, is poisonous. Nothing can kill your self-esteem faster than comparing yourself to someone else's success and deciding that you are a failure. I don't mean using someone else as an example of what is possible–that's actually an awesome way to improve yourself. No, I mean using someone else's success to beat yourself up for not being good enough. The worst part is, you might not even realize you're doing it. Whenever I hear someone say "That was a terrible run. I should have run much faster" or "I can't keep up with everyone else, so I'm not even going to try," my heart breaks a little. I also get kinda pissed off at their mean girl.

Other people's performance is their business. It is a result of their hard work, yes, but also a result of how they felt that day, the weather, their internal self-talk, what they ate for breakfast, how much sleep they got, and a million other factors. It has nothing to do with you and in no way reduces your accomplishment.

The same goes for how you ran last week, last month, or last year vs. today. Some days the stars align and the experience is nothing short of euphoric, while other days it will be a battle just to get out the door. This is completely normal! As I mentioned above, if you track your performance over months–not days or weeks–

you'll see improvement. Realize that developing a running habit takes time (heck, it took me almost fifteen years to make mine stick!) and that you might even go months at a time without running. This is also completely normal, and, I would venture to say, probably a good thing, because it allows you to appreciate the differences in your body and mind when you're running regularly and when you're not. Eventually, the discomfort of not running will be greater than the discomfort of running. That's when you'll know you've got a lifetime habit.

Find the good in every single run, even if it is as simple as saying "I ran today."

TAKING IT TO
THE NEXT LEVEL

"In running, it doesn't matter whether you come in first, in the middle of the pack, or last. You can say, 'I have finished.' There is a lot of satisfaction in that."
–Fred Lebow, co-founder,
New York City Marathon

Did you know that women weren't allowed to participate in the track and field portion of the Olympics until 1928? And that the first women's Olympic marathon wasn't held until 1988? As ridiculous as it sounds today, at the time running was considered too strenuous for women. Fortunately for you and I, things have changed a lot since then–women now represent a sizable portion of the field in any footrace, and we are kicking ass.

Should you give racing a try? In my opinion, yes. To start with, a race can be a lot of fun. It's the ultimate group workout, with people lining the streets to cheer you on, plus you always get a free t-shirt! As a motivational tool, knowing that you have to run a specific distance on a specific date can't be beat. And when those annoying runners in your office can't stop talking about their weekend activities, you'll finally have something to contribute to the conversation.

But really, a race is the perfect opportunity to push your limits and really see what you're capable of achieving. The thrill of running with a crowd of like-minded humans, all going in the same direction, striving together to achieve the same goal is simply incredible. A primal instinct you didn't even know you had is activated, and the energy of the group elevates you to new levels. If you didn't feel like a runner before your first race, you'll definitely feel like one afterwards.

What can you expect at your first race? A lot depends on the distance and the number of people running. Shorter races, such as 1-mile "fun runs" or 5K (five kilometers, or 3.1 miles) distances tend to attract smaller crowds and have fewer runners. A local 5K might have as few as twenty-five entrants, but if it is a popular event, that number might be 1,000 or more. In a shorter race, you're also likely to encounter a combination of runners and walkers, especially for charity events, and the atmosphere is usually very relaxed and supportive.

Mid-to-long-distances, such as the half-marathon (13.1 miles) or marathon (26.2 miles) tend to be larger events, especially in major metropolitan areas. Expect the number of runners to be well over 1,000, and commonly over 10,000. Well-established events such as the New York Marathon are so popular that a lottery system has been established to ensure everyone has a fair chance to snag one of the 47,000 spots at the starting line. And no, that's not a typo. Forty-seven thousand people, all running simultaneously, for 26.2 miles. Thousands upon thousands of spectators turn out to watch, making the experience truly memorable for everyone. It's definitely on my bucket list.

If you love the idea of a timed race, but don't relish the thought of running with hundreds or thousands of other people by your side (or you live in a part of the country where races are hard to find) consider a virtual race - an event that allows you to run your distance where and when you want, and still get an awesome finisher's medal!

For a great selection of virtual races with fabulous medals visit www.RWCVirtualRaces.com

Perhaps you don't care for the idea of being timed, but still want the joy of running with others? Consider joining the recent trend of 5K run/walk events where there is no clock, such as a color run. These activities are pretty much just a big party disguised as a workout: fun and sweaty, with snacks. You still get the t-shirt along with a lot of great memories, but nobody knows how long it took you to cross the finish line. Not even you!

Before you sign up for your first event, do your research on seasonal weather, terrain, distance, location, size and rules. Almost every race has its own website with this information. Ask around (or do an online search) for anyone else that has run it in the past, to find out if it has typically been well-organized.

Choose a training plan based on your current fitness level, then stick to it as much as possible. Think of training for a race like studying for a test. Cramming it all in the night before won't result in your best performance, and the same goes for a 5K. Do your homework, study a little every week, and you'll be much happier with the final outcome. I like to think of a race as a really fun reward for all the hard work I've done in the previous weeks and months. But don't worry too much about whether you've picked the perfect training schedule. The human body responds to physical stress by getting stronger, and for beginners, almost any consistent and progressive plan will work.

The most challenging part of your training will be mental. Sometimes, after weeks, or even months, of training, it can start to feel a lot like a job. A really sweaty job with no pay and no dental plan. When this happens, allow yourself to rediscover the joy of running by giving yourself permission to take a break. Missing a couple workouts (not ten) does not mean you'll lose strength and endurance–quite the opposite, in fact. Taking a short rest during a long training plan can often translate into better performance, better sleep, and higher quality workouts in the end.

Throughout your training, it is also likely that you'll feel nervous, worried, and anxious about race day. This is completely normal, even for veteran runners. Ask yourself why you are nervous. If you're worried about finishing, you have no need to be concerned. You will definitely finish. You've been training for weeks, possibly months, and you know you can go the distance. If it gets too hard, you'll slow down. You've got this.

Are you worried about finishing in a certain time? Stop right there. If this is your first race, whatever time you get will be a personal record. If not, try to understand why that particular time is so important to you, and what you think that means if you fail. Does it take away from the achievement of running this race? No. Does it take away from the achievement of training for this race? No. Does it mean you aren't a fit, healthy, amazing woman? Again, no. It just means that on that day, in those circumstances, that's how fast you ran. Nothing more, nothing less. You can always try again.

If you are concerned about what other people will think about your time, you are wasting your thoughts and creating unnecessary pain for yourself. Other people will think what they want and you can't do anything about it– the only thing you can control is your own mind. And really, most of them are probably thinking "Wow, I wish I could do that." So relax, slow down, and enjoy the process. The race is just the icing on the cake. The real work is what you're doing right now. And you're working your butt off, so be proud!

When race day comes, make sure you've double-checked the race rules. There are usually requirements for placement of your number, whether you can wear headphones, and where to place your timing chip, to name a few. If you don't follow them, you risk being disqualified.

Get to the starting line at least a half-hour early to hit up the Port-a-Potties and assess the situation. If you're slow, you'll want to start at the back of the pack. Nothing feels worse than hearing the starting gun go off and feeling the pressure of hundreds of people trying to push past you all at once. Larger races will corral you by anticipated race pace, and start you off in waves to make sure that everyone gets a fair chance. Don't worry about being too far back– you can always pass people later as the field thins out! And it feels a lot better to catch up to other people than it does to have everyone in the entire race pass you by. Fact.

Once you've crossed the starting line, the race is yours to enjoy. Savor each moment, connect with the fans, talk to others along the route, and encourage everyone you see, especially if they seem to be struggling. And if it happens to be you in last place, who cares? Finishing is finishing, regardless of how long it took. There is no shame in the back of the pack. Just remember to smile for the camera as you cross the finish line!

And speaking of the back of the pack, I have a personal story to share about one of my favorite races: the 2003 Presidential Run in Reading, Pennsylvania, a small 5K with only about fifty people. At the time, I had been running consistently for over a year, and was looking forward to seeing what I could do. My husband decided to join me for moral support and as we lined up at the start, I surveyed the rest of the runners, most of whom looked pretty experienced. There were no other chunky monkeys like me, but I did notice a much older woman dressed in a purple track suit and thought "Yes. I am going to Take. Her. Down."

The gun went off, and within about two minutes, I was dead last. The woman in purple left me in the dust! It was a tiny bit humiliating (especially after I found out she was seventy-two years old) but overall I was pretty happy just to be running on that autumn day. The weather was beautiful–cold, crisp and clear–and the course was on a lovely trail next to the Schuylkill River. As I approached the finish line, at approximately forty-two minutes, my husband kindly slowed down so that I wouldn't be in last place. That's the real spirit of running. And the woman in purple? I still think of her to this day, as an example of what is possible. In thirty years, that will be me (but my track suit will be hot pink).

DRESS FOR SUCCESS

If you dress like a runner, you'll feel like a runner. I'm not saying you need to buy $200 running shoes, or those ridiculous shorts that are slit so far up the side you can see tan lines. I just mean that if you wear clothes designed for running, you'll be a lot more comfortable, which will help you stay motivated to keep doing it. Also, have you ever heard the phrase "fake it til you make it"? That applies here. Dress the part long enough, and you'll start to believe it.

Beginners tend to wear whatever is already in the closet. This might be a big baggy T-shirt and sweats, or it might be a foxy little spandex number with matching leg warmers leftover from your Jazzercise days …

No? Just me? OK, then, moving on.

It is completely normal to hesitate before investing in a new wardrobe for a habit you're not even sure you want to maintain, but after a few runs, it's time to take the plunge. You might even realize that running is a fantastic excuse to go shopping. The problem is, it's really easy to spend a fortune on gear that seemed like a good idea at the time, but ends up at the back of your closet after a couple workouts. Hopefully, this chapter will help you avoid some of those rookie mistakes, and all of your purchases will become well-used favorites over time.

Before we get too far into this discussion, however, I need to warn you–there will be some tough love ahead, as well as some frank discussion about the challenges of dressing a larger body for running. Some of you might feel anxiety, or perhaps even righteous anger while reading the next few pages. Please take my words in the spirit they are intended, which is to help you pump up your self-esteem and body confidence, feel great while you run, and simplify your life.

The first lesson? Stop using your clothes to hide your body when you run, and quit worrying about what others think. Nobody else is even looking at you while you run. Seriously. Most people are far too concerned about themselves to give you even a passing glance–they are thinking about their own workout, when that cute guy is going to call, or where to go for dinner. Unless you're wearing a sequined bodysuit and matching tutu or singing along to Beyonce at the top of your lungs, nobody cares.

LOCK AND LOAD

When you run, your breasts move up and down as well as side to side. For you lucky A and B cups out there, this is mostly just an inconvenience. But if you're a C or higher, all of that extra motion can cause back pain and throw your gait out of whack. That's why a sports bra is arguably the most important piece of running gear any woman needs. If you don't take any other advice I've given you in this book, heed this: your girls need proper support when you run. And by that I mean: Strap. Them. Down. Otherwise, they're going to fly around like a Baywatch lifeguard running down the beach in a bikini. Bouncing boobs might look sexy on TV, but in real life, they hurt. Big or small, if they're not properly immobilized when you're moving, you're going to suffer.

Unfortunately, good support isn't cheap. Expect to pay upwards of $50 if you have a lot on top. And here's more bad news: an effective sports bra is all about fit and function, with fashion trailing a distant third. Oh, the sacrifices we make for this sport! But unless you're planning to run shirtless, nobody will know what your bra looks like.

Invest in a few really good bras and take good care of them, and they will last you a long time. Choose one made primarily from a synthetic blend (with little to no cotton) that doesn't have much too much stretch (stretch equals bounce), and make sure it is rated as a motion-control bra. Padded, wide straps are best for larger breasts, while smaller girls can get away with racerback, pullover styles. Get measured (or follow the instructions on the website) to make sure you're getting the right size. If you're spilling out of it everywhere, this defeats the purpose. More coverage means more control. Personally, I won't run in anything but an Enell–if it's good enough for Oprah, it's good enough for me! While it won't win any style awards–think "straight jacket meets corset" – when I'm wearing one of these treasures, it feels as if a weight has literally been lifted off my chest. It's that effective. Moving Comfort has a great line too, and if you do an online search for "motion control bra" you'll find plenty of options.

And just in case you're not fully convinced, here's a cautionary tale: A few years back, I joined a friend in a 5K Mother's Day run. The morning of the race, she said that she planned to walk most of it, so I opted not to wear my trusty Enell, and instead wore a regular bra. However, when the adrenaline of the event kicked in, so did her running mojo – and she took off like a shot. She's 5'10" with loooong legs, so I was hustling like a madwoman just to keep up. I'm sure you can imagine the frenetic (and painful) bouncing that ensued. We crossed the finish line at a full-out run, and the camera captured me smiling from ear to ear, in mid bounce, left breast up high, right one down low. It is one of the funniest photos I've ever seen of myself, and a solid reminder that a good sports-bra is critical.

IF THE SHOE FITS

Shoes are the next most important decision. Choosing the perfect running shoe is not easy. Everyone's foot is different, and adding even more complexity to the issue is the question of what kind of runner you are. Do you over- or under-pronate? Are you a heel-striker or do you land more towards the ball of your foot? How much do you weigh? Do you prefer a soft cushy shoe or one with a more minimalist feel? There too many factors at play to allow me to offer succinct advice on how to choose the perfect shoe for you, so instead I'm going to refer you to your local running store. They're the experts.

A reputable brick-and-mortar store will measure your feet, analyze your gait, and discuss your weekly mileage and typical running surfaces before making a recommendation. In addition, they should allow you to run a short distance in the shoes, perhaps around the parking lot or on a treadmill in the store. And most importantly, they will accept returns. Running shoes are not cheap! You need to know that you have the option to bring them back and exchange for something else if it just doesn't work out. Ask a lot of questions, and understand the store policies before you buy. Online merchants, such as RoadRunner.com, have incredibly generous return policies, great prices and a huge selection.

A word of caution about the "minimalist" (shoes with a very thin sole and little to no difference in height between the toes and the heel) trend that is currently sweeping the running world: although they are a great concept, this type of shoe is not always the friend of a heavier girl. If you've spent most of your exercise time in traditional sneakers, your ankles and feet might not be strong enough to handle the lack of support in minimalist shoes–and you might find yourself quickly sidelined with a painful overuse injury such as plantar fasciitis. Believe me, you do *not* want to deal with that! If you're interested, do your research into this type of shoe first, and if you decide to go forward with a pair, introduce them very slowly to your routine. Make sure to include lots of ankle and foot strengthening exercises (done in your bare feet) on your strength training days, and wear supportive shoes at all other times. You'll thank me later.

And while we're on the topic of footwear, let's talk about socks. Most of the time, socks are an afterthought, but they're actually pretty important! If they are too big or too small, too thick or too thin, you can end up with blisters. If they're 100% cotton, and you tend to have sweaty feet, you'll end up with … you guessed it, blisters again. Blisters hurt, and when your feet hurt, you stop running.

Good socks are worth the extra cash, and in the grand scheme of things they're not a huge investment. Your local running store can guide you to the ones that will work for you. Plan to spend around $10-15 a pair and pick up at least three so you can get a week's worth of runs before you need to wash them.

YOU'RE NOT FOOLING ANYONE

When it comes to workout clothes, and running gear in particular, wearing stuff that fits properly is critical. Why? Because if it isn't comfortable, your workout will suck. You'll either be messing around with your clothes the whole time, trying to adjust them to feel right, or you'll be so miserable that you'll quit early. Also, nobody wants to see you picking a wedgie on the treadmill. Seriously. Don't be that person.

Make sure your clothes fit your *current* body–not the body you wish you had, or one that is three sizes larger than you are right now. It really doesn't matter how fabulous that neon racerback tank is, if your ta-tas are threatening to fly out of it with every step, your run is going to be a short one. Save that stuff for Zumba.

Most of the fit issues I've seen are of the "If I wear a ginormous shirt and baggy sweats, nobody will know I'm fat" variety. While I appreciate not wanting to wear clothes that cling like plastic wrap to your least favorite body parts, going too big is definitely *not* the answer. Too much fabric, especially 100% cotton, gets in the way of proper movement, bunches up in unpleasant places, and traps heat and moisture. Poorly fitted garments can also mean a lot of skin-to-skin contact–such as between thighs, or between your upper arms and the side of your body. All that rubbing ultimately leads to chafing, which causes painful, red welts on your skin. Chafing sucks. If your sweat can't evaporate properly, your skin will get rubbed raw, and this may keep you from running. Later on, I'll go into more detail on how to prevent chafing, but it starts with wearing clothes that fit.

Here's more tough love: if you think those huge t-shirts that hang to your knees make you look smaller, you're mistaken. You're not fooling anyone aside from yourself. Instead of camouflaging your size, they emphasize the biggest parts of your body, giving the illusion that your body is a huge pillow. Dressing this way also shouts to the world that you're ashamed of your body. Is that really the message you want to send? Drop the security blanket and rock your curves. Wear a short-sleeved shirt, or (gasp!) a tank top, and let your knees see the light of day! You are beautiful and amazing exactly the way you are right now. Show others that you care about yourself by choosing clothes that fit.

And speaking of your knees, we need to talk about tights. What you wear on your bottom half is possibly even more important than the top. Simply put, if you wear yoga pants, loose shorts, or sweatpants to run, you leave yourself open to chafing from the seams between your thighs. Anything that doesn't hug your legs is going to ride up, which means you'll spend a lot of time tugging them back down. It sucks, and it's completely avoidable if you wear running tights. They fit like a glove and move with you instead of rubbing against your skin, which will save you a lot of pain and suffering. I know you're cringing right now at the thought of wearing something so form-fitting in public, but you're going to have to trust me on this one. Tights come in several different lengths, from mid-thigh to ankle, so you should have no problem finding something that suits you. And here's some great news: they actually make you look thinner, because they don't add bulk. They also keep jiggling to a minimum while you're moving. Pair your tights with a shirt that hits below your hips if you're concerned about covering your tummy or butt. And if you're still feeling over-exposed, consider a running skirt, which combines tights with a skirt that hangs to mid-thigh. These have been rising in popularity lately with several manufacturers offering really cute options.

SHOP TIL YOU DROP

Before you hop in your car to head to the mall, you'll need to think about where you're most likely to find your size range. If you're a size L or smaller, you'll be able to shop anywhere, but those of you that wear an XL or larger may have to look a little harder. Personally, I find this to be somewhat ironic. Society tells us that we need a thin body to be accepted, but then makes it difficult to find cute clothing appropriate to do the very activity that will help us get there. It's maddening.

Fortunately, over the past few years, several forward-thinking companies have taken note that "plus-size" women actually *do* exercise, and are willing to spend their hard-earned dollars to do be comfortable and stylish while doing so. If you search online for "Plus Size Workout Clothing" you'll get page after page of results.

Be aware, however, that many of these places either have a limited selection of larger sizes in-store or only offer online sales. If you do need to purchase through a website, order in more than one size and color, so that you're saved the hassle of exchanging things through the mail. Returns are often free, but check the website policy just to be sure. Anyplace that has a brick-and-mortar store, such as Old Navy, will usually allow you to return your online purchases directly to the store. When you find a product line that seems to be made just for you, stock up!

Get a roundup of the best plus-size running gear, including size ranges, price ranges, shipping and return policies:
www.RunningWithCurves.net/
Shopping-Guide

MATERIAL GIRL

Finding clothes that fit properly is more than half the battle, but fabric is extremely important too. As I mentioned above, cotton traps sweat, which can lead to a pretty miserable workout. The ideal material for running gear (including undies!) is a light, soft, synthetic blend that draws moisture away from your skin and dries quickly. Anything you wear on your bottom half will ideally have a lot of stretch to it as well. Avoid anything that's made mostly of cotton.

Most running clothes are now made from "wicking" (also known as technical) fabrics which are designed to pull sweat away from your body to speed evaporation. The most important thing is that it be lightweight and dry quickly. If you pull your technical shirt out of the washing machine after the spin cycle and it feels almost dry, this is a good indicator that it will work well for you during a hot, sweaty run.

CARING FOR YOUR CLOTHES

Your running clothes (especially those sports bras) weren't cheap, so make the most of your money by caring for them properly. Always wash in cold water and never, ever put them in the dryer. Heat breaks down Spandex and Lycra, shortening their lifespan. Hang them on a rack when they come out of the washer and they'll be ready to wear in a few hours.

And when you're done with your workout, for Pete's sake, don't let your investment sit in a dark, closed hamper for days! Sweaty clothes are the perfect environment for bacteria to grow, and if you let them stew too long, they'll start to smell pretty ripe. At the very least, make sure to drop your clothes in an open basket, which will allow them to dry. And if you do find that your gear has an odor, soak it in a vinegar solution for a few hours and rewash.

PREVENTION OF CHAFING

Chafing is the bane of all runners, not just those that are overweight. Fortunately, there are many products to help you manage this uncomfortable problem. In addition to finding clothes that fit, look for shirts and tights with flat seams, and socks with minimal seams.

Bodyglide is an anti-chafing substance that looks a little like stick deodorant. Once applied, it feels completely dry, is invisible and odorless, and is resistant to sweat. Apply it anywhere seams irritate your skin, where you have skin-to-skin contact, or on those places on your feet that tend to rub against your shoes. You won't even know it's there, except when you undress after your run and realize you don't have angry red patches anywhere on your body! There are other products that have similar effects, but in my experience Bodyglide is the best. And definitely avoid Vaseline or any other petroleum jelly. Yes, it will reduce friction. It will also stain your clothes and feel sticky. Yuck!

Moleskin is an adhesive felt-like material that sticks to your skin and provides a barrier against friction. It is commonly used on the feet, but you can use it wherever you feel you need more protection than just Bodyglide. For example, when I use my iPod armband, the edge of the strap rubs the inside of my arm raw. I place a small piece of moleskin right where the strap hits and Voila! Problem solved. It can be cut to any size and removes easily when your workout is done. If you're in a pinch and don't have any moleskin, a bandaid or athletic tape will work.

GADGETS AND OTHER FUN STUFF

What you choose to wear and bring with you on your run can help maintain your fitness mojo - or end up being a giant pain in the ass. For example, I used to tie my house key to my shoe laces, and then spend my entire run getting annoyed as it flopped around with every step. Nowadays, manufacturers are adding thoughtful details to their clothing lines, such as waistband key pockets, in an attempt to differentiate themselves from the pack. This is great news for you, because a functional garment can remove those pesky excuses for skipping a run, such as "I have no place to put my iPod". When you're shopping, look for things like reflective strips, built-in pockets for a phone or MP3 player and extra-long sleeves with thumbholes to keep your hands warm in the winter. Or consider a lightweight wristband with a key/ID pocket. You can find them at most running stores, or look around on Pinterest to find instructions on making your own.

In addition to functional running gear, there are countless gadgets out there that allow you to gather data about your workouts. If you've got a smartphone with GPS, you can download an app (such as RunKeeper) that tracks how fast and far you ran, with the added bonus of calling out interval cues along the way. If you get lost, the GPS can lead you right back home. Training for a 5K? Download a C25K app to give you daily training plans.

If you don't want to carry a smartphone while you run, but still want the benefits of GPS, try a GPS watch that does all of the above while attached to your wrist. They are a bit bigger than a regular watch, but still lightweight enough that you won't notice it. After you run, stats are downloaded to your computer so you can review them with ease. The downside? Cost. Technology isn't cheap.

Don't care about GPS but still want to time your intervals? Go old school with a running watch (such as the Timex Ironman), or pick up a simple, inexpensive and sweat-proof clip-on timer like the GymBoss.

Pedometers have come a long way in the past five years. For about $100, you can get a model that saves your step data electronically so you can track your activity over time with a web-based program and smartphone app. Some will even monitor your sleep and link to food-tracking services like MyFitnessPal. My favorite device is the FitBit, but there are lots of other choices. Take note, however, that these devices are intended to count steps and can only estimate your distance. So if you need an accurate measurement of how far and fast you've gone, a GPS watch or smartphone app is a better choice.

Heart rate monitors are another popular tool with runners, because they give you a good understanding of how hard your cardio-respiratory system is working when you run. You can get a simple system for under $100, which includes a wrist unit so you can easily keep an eye on your heart rate while you're running.

One caveat to using all this cool gear: keep it simple. If it takes you a half-hour to get yourself ready to run, you've probably got too much going on (or else you're a master at delay tactics). Running toys should motivate you to get out the door, not get in the way. So if you find yourself fiddling around with all of your gadgets instead of actually running, try subtracting a few to see how it goes.

DEALING WITH INJURIES

Truly addicted runners love talking about two things: their stats, and their injuries. Although you might never torture your coworkers with every last detail about your weekend 5K, the sad truth is that at some point in the future, you're likely to experience a body issue that requires rest and healing. If you're lucky, your injuries will be mild and resolve quickly. Many of you will not be so fortunate, however, and you'll need to deal with the annoyance of taking a break from your beloved routine. This is the reality of any sport based on repetitive motion, but it doesn't mean you are doomed to failure.

In fifteen years of running I've had a lot of injuries. Achilles tendinitis, patellar tendinitis, plantar fasciitis, shin splints, bruised toes, IT band issues ... you name it, it seems like I've had it, and managed my way through it. The main lesson I've learned? Injuries heal if you let them. The problem is, taking the time to let them heal can be a big challenge.

Pain is your body's way of telling you it needs attention. Your body is smart! Listen to what it says, and learn the difference between discomfort, the voice of your inner mean girl and actual pain. You can run through discomfort and you should *always* ignore the negative voices in your head, but nine times out of ten you should not run through pain.

When you think you're injured, or have a chronic pain that just won't go away, do your research. There are countless resources available online or in books. Ask other runners or stop by your local running store. Make an appointment with a specialist or physical therapist. The more you know, the more effective you can be in your recovery plan.

Forcing yourself to take a break, even if it's just for a week, is not always easy. You've just gotten yourself into a routine that you love and it feels amazing. You're afraid that if you lose your momentum you'll never get back on track. You feel angry, frustrated, and defeated. This is a chance for your mean girl to step up, telling you that your body has betrayed you, that you've failed yet again, and that you'll never be a real runner. The next thing you know, a week of rest has turned into three months of cupcake and wine-fueled pity parties–and you've proven all of those mean thoughts true. How do I know? Because I've been there. Many times.

To the negative mind, rest and quitting look a lot alike. They both involve not running, sometimes losing hard-won endurance and aerobic capacity, and perhaps even weight gain. But that's where the similarities end. Quitting is a result of giving up, negative thinking, and loss of confidence. Rest is a result of loving your body enough to care for it properly. If taking a break from running for a few weeks or months means the difference between full recovery, or causing further damage (and potentially not running ever again), the choice is clear. So if you want to be a runner for the next twenty-plus years, set yourself up for success by taking care of your body right now.

There's no need to panic about losing fitness during a rest break. Just because you can't run doesn't necessarily mean you can't exercise. Find another activity that doesn't aggravate your injury, such as walking, pool running, yoga, cycling, swimming, rowing–even the elliptical machine is better than nothing–to maintain a baseline fitness level. After you're cleared to start running again, I guarantee you will get back to your pre-injury levels of fitness, and that you will lose any weight you gained. It might not happen overnight, but there's no rush. You'll do it the same way you did the first time around: with consistency, patience and time. In the meantime, the rest might do your body a world of good, allowing everything to rejuvenate–not just the damaged parts.

And while you're resting? Stretch. A lot. You should always stretch after every workout, but it's even more important when you're taking a break to heal. Muscles can get extremely tight when they don't get much exercise, so spend a few minutes a day working on this aspect of your fitness and it will be much easier to get back into your groove when the time comes.

The reality is that you will probably get injured at some point. Expect it, take the time you need to heal and you'll come out stronger than before.

SAFETY GEAR

Unless all of your running is done on a treadmill, safety gear is something you need to understand. If you're running near traffic, you need make yourself as visible as possible to oncoming drivers. Wear bright clothes and/or a reflective vest, attach a blinking light to your shirt, choose garments with reflective strips–anything to draw attention to your presence on the side of the road. If you're running in a poorly lit area after dark, use a small headlamp to see where you're going. Finally, always carry ID with you, either a driver's license or an identifying wristband (such as RoadID) with your name, emergency contact, and medical alerts.

NUTRITION

Everyone's body is different, and there is no single nutritional plan that fits all. That being said, there are a few basic rules to follow to ensure your best performance:

- Feed yourself the highest quality fuel possible, at all times. This means avoiding processed foods, eating lots of fruits, vegetables and high quality protein, sticking to complex carbs (rather than highly refined grains and sugar) and–yes, really–including some fat in your diet. I like to follow Michael Pollan's rule of thumb: If your great-grandmother wouldn't recognize it as food, don't eat it.

- A hydrated body performs better, so drink a fair amount of water each day. Unless you're running for two hours or more, or have a diagnosed electrolyte deficiency, you do not need to rehydrate with a sports drink. They are mostly just sugar. Stick to plain water, or add fruit for flavor.

- Avoid big meals in the couple hours before a run—if you're hungry, have a small snack such as a piece of fruit or a handful of nuts instead. Unless you're planning to run for more than an hour, your muscles should have enough stored fuel to get you through your workout on an empty stomach. Your body diverts blood flow away from non-essential organs when you're exercising, to make sure your muscles are properly supplied with oxygen. This includes your digestive track. That means any food that isn't easily absorbed will lie like a rock in your stomach while you run, because your body is busy doing other things. It is no fun to run with a bellyache. It's even less fun to stop running so you can puke.

- Consume alcohol in moderation, and never, ever, before a run, because it clouds your judgment and impairs your reflexes. Alcohol dehydrates your body and contains no real nutritive value (except for red wine, which I consider to be an essential food group). I prefer to avoid it completely for the couple days leading up to a big race or extra long run.

CONCLUSION

If you've made it this far, you're either over-the-moon excited to get busy with your new running addiction, or you're determined to get your money's worth. Either way, thanks for sticking with me to the end.

If I've done my job, I've convinced you that running will help you build up your self-esteem and make you feel like a rock star. Just beware–running is like a drug. If you use it regularly, you might get hooked. The addiction process has four stages:

1. Experimentation

Self-explanatory. At this point, running is just a way to mix up your workout routine, have a little fun, and find out what all the fuss is about. You might run a couple times a month, and it feels pretty good. What's the harm in experimenting, right?

2. Regular use

Now you're running a few times a week–because you really, reeeaaallly, like it. It's possible that you're hanging out with some new friends, people that spend a lot of time running, talking about running, and reading about running. You've begun to invest in running paraphernalia, and you're speaking the lingo: "Dude, I had such a great tempo run this weekend. It felt like I was flying!"

3. Risky use

It's getting all kinds of crazy up in here. You've rearranged your work schedule to make sure you can run at lunch, and curtail your drinking on nights before an early morning run. On Christmas morning, your family waits patiently to open presents while you get your run in. Withdrawal symptoms appear when you have to skip a few days. Your old friends are starting to ask questions, and considering an intervention.

4. Dependency

At this point, you're beyond help. The addiction has infiltrated every aspect of your life. Your skin is glowing, self-confidence oozes from your pores, and you are actively recruiting others to your lifestyle.

Obviously, I'm in stage four.

In all seriousness, though, what I hope you've learned from our time together is that you absolutely *can* be a runner in the body you have right now. You are not too fat, your legs are not too short, and your fitness level is right where it needs to be. Runners come in all shapes, sizes, and abilities. There's room for everyone.

And since I'm terrible at goodbyes, I'm just going to leave you with a top ten list (in the grand traditions of both David Letterman and Moses). Call it the Ten Commandments of Running, if you like:

10. If you run, you are a runner.
9. Running is uncomfortable. Not impossible. You're capable of much more than you know.
8. It doesn't matter how many times you start over. Running will always be there for you.

7. Find your bliss. Understand why you run, or why you *want* to run. Make a list, keep adding to it over time, and refer to it regularly.

6. The back of the pack is a great place to be. Seriously.

5. Consistency, patience, and time get results. Your body will improve at its own pace, and if you stick with it, you'll get there. Don't rush it. Savor the journey.

4. If you fail to plan, you plan to fail. Expect the unexpected, and be ready.

3. Stop worrying about what everyone else thinks about you. Their opinion of you is not the problem–your opinion is the only one that counts. Start believing you are awesome, and you will be.

2. Find the good in every single run, even if it is as simple as saying "I ran today."

And finally,

1. Be the seventy-two-year old woman in the purple track suit, or the 300-pound woman in last place. Be an example of what is possible. You never know who you might inspire.

Stick to these guidelines, and you'll have many fabulous miles ahead of you.

To make the most of your running experience, grab one (or all!) of these free gifts from my website:

The Running With Curves Manifesto:
www.RunningWithCurves.net/Manifesto

Plus-Size Running Gear Shopping Guide:
www.RunningWithCurves.net/Shopping-Guide

1-Week Jumpstart Training Plan:
www.RunningWithCurves.net/Jumpstart

Ready to take it to the next level?
Join the Virtual Running Club!
www.RunningWithCurves.net/JoinTheCommunity

or sign up for a virtual race:
www.RWCVirtualRaces.com

GRATITUDE

This book could not have happened without the help, wisdom, love and kindness of the many fabulous people in my life! I am humbled and grateful beyond measure by your unwavering support.

First and foremost, to my amazing husband Ken: Thank you for sticking by my side, encouraging me, supporting me, and for reading every word I write. I love you.

To my parents: Thank you for loving me and teaching me that I can do or be anything I want. I wish you were here to see what you set in motion.

To Martha, Tom, Kerry, Paul and Lenna: You are the best siblings a girl could hope for. Thank you for always being there with a kind word and for believing in me. It means more than you could ever know.

To Abby, Amanda, Gina, McKenzie and Nina: Thank you for sharing your own personal thoughts on running, and for allowing me to put them out there in the world. Your words will help so many others. They most certainly helped me.

To Angela and Kris: Thank you for bringing this book from dream to reality. I could not have done this without you. You have changed my life.

To Rena: Thank you for being you. I would not be on this path if I had not met you. I am eternally grateful.

To *ALL* of my family, friends and clients, both near and far: Thank you for the never-ending encouragement. Thank you for the emails, for listening, for talking it out, for reading my work, for sharing it with everyone you know, and for sending your positive energy my way. There have been times over the past few months when I've struggled with writing, with training for a half-marathon, or just generally questioned my life path. At those moments, I often hear a quiet voice in my head telling me to keep going. I know these voices are coming from all of you. It is amazing to have such a fabulous support system.

To every single stranger that has ever cheered me on during a race, or shouted 'keep up the good work' when they see me chugging along, THANK YOU.

To my own body - legs, heart, lungs and all the rest - you rock. Thank you for not giving up.

ABOUT THE AUTHOR

Jill Angie is a runner, triathlete, writer, virtual race director and personal trainer who wants to live in a world where everyone is free to feel fit and fabulous at any size. She started the Running With Curves movement in 2013 to show that runners come in all shapes, sizes and speeds, and since then has assembled a global community of revolutionaries that are taking the running world by storm. If you would like to be part of the Curvolution, visit www.RunningWithCurves.net to find out more!

ABOUT DIFFERENCE PRESS

Difference Press offers life coaches, other healing professionals, a comprehensive solution to get their book written, published, and promoted. A boutique style alternative to self-publishing, Difference Press boasts a fair and easy to understand profit structure, low priced author copies, and author-friendly contract terms. Founder, Angela Lauria has been bringing the literary ventures of authors-in-transformation to life since 1994.

Your Delicious Book

If you're like many of the authors we work with, you have wanted to write a book for a long time, maybe you have even started a book … or two… or three … but somehow, as hard as you have tried to make your book a priority other things keep getting in the way.

It's not just finding the time and confidence to write that is an obstacle. The logistics of finding an editor, hiring an experienced designer, and figuring out all the technicalities of publishing stops many authors-in-transformation from writing a book that makes a difference. Your Delicious Book is designed to address every obstacle along the way so all you have to do is write!

Tackling the technical end of publishing

The comprehensive coaching, editing, design, publishing and marketing services offered by Difference Press mean that your book will be edited by a pro, designed by an experienced graphic artist, and published digitally and in print by publishing industry experts. We handle all of the technical aspects of your book creation so you can spend more of your time focusing on your business.

Ready to write your book?

Visit www.YourDeliciousBook.com. When you apply mention you are Difference Press reader and get 10% off the program price.

OTHER BOOKS BY DIFFERENCE PRESS

Agile!: The Half-Assed Guide To Creating Anything You Want From Scratch. No Experts Required!
by Sasha Mobley

Fat Be Gone: Four Steps To Permanent Weight Loss And True Happiness
by Carleasa Coates

Zen and the Art of Making a Morris Chair: Awaken Your Creative Potential
by Randy Gafner

Craving Love: A Girlfriend's Guide Out of Divorce Hell into Heaven and A New Life You Love
by Shelly Young Modes

Sex, Lies & Creativity: Improve Innovation Skills And Enhance Innovation Culture By Understanding Gender Diversity & Creative Thinking
by Julia Roberts

Woman Overboard! Six Ways Women Avoid Conflict And One Way To Live Drama-Free
by Rachel Alexandria

Mafia\Kitten Lessons For Strong Women On Finally Letting Go, Feeling Safe, And Being Loved
by Valerie LaPenta Steiger

Tapping Into Past Lives Heal Soul Traumas and Claim Your Spiritual Gifts with Quantum EFT
by Jenny Johnston

THANK YOU

Thank you for reading this book. It was a true labor of love, and if it affected you in some way, I invite you to share your thoughts by writing a review on Amazon or contacting me at Jill@RunningWithCurves.net.

CONTACT INFO/SOCIAL MEDIA

Jill@RunningWithCurves.net

RunningWithCurves.net

Facebook.com/RunningWithCurves

Instagram.com/RunningWithCurves

Printed in Great Britain
by Amazon

The Guide

First Edition.
Published in Great Britain by Mindspace Press.

Author: Adam Dacey
Copyright Mindspace 2019

Typeset: Sakura Dao
Proofreader: Lyndsay Hill
Cover Design: Tian Du
Copyeditor: Hannah Danson
Drawing of the author on page 206: Joan Hendy
Illustration on page 207: Elsa Houghton

Printed and bound in Cornwall, England by TJ International.
The paper used is wood-free, Munken Premium Cream
Font used: Garamond

A CIP catalogue record for this book is available from the British Library.
ISBN: 978-1-9164838-0-4
Second Printing. January 2019.

Mindspace Press
Moseley Exchange
149 Alcester Rd
Moseley
Birmingham, B13 8JP

For more information, online resources, questions, and review, please contact:
info@mindspace.org.uk, 07908950871, www.mindspace.org.uk

Guide to the **Mindful** Way of Life

MINDSPACE PRESS

Adam Dacey

CONTENTS

MINDFUL LISTENING   1

Enjoying practices that naturally bring us to the present moment while enhancing our communication with the world

CHAPTER 2
MINDFUL BODY

How to abide in the present moment

Mindful Hands: Sitting & Standing
Relaxing meditations to bring instant stress relief and calm

Mindful Body Scan
Take your time training the mind to focus and release tension

Mindful Pain Relief
Utilising the power of our mind to heal the body

Clear Body
Introducing a simple, helpful visualisation

Mindful Anchor
Learning to ground ourselves into the present moment

...

CHAPTER 3
MINDFUL BREATHING

Pacify stress with a series of essential breathing meditations

...

CHAPTER 4
MINDFUL MIND

Developing emotional intelligence and stillness

Allowing our mind to settle and thoughts to harmonise

Abide within the moment

Letting clouds of distraction pass through the sky of our mind

Using an ancient visualisation to take our practice deeper

Incorporating all the practices we have learned thus far

...

CHAPTER 5
MINDFUL MOVEMENT

Establishing a dynamic mindfulness practice

Combining our walking with the breathing

Moving naturally into the moment

...

CHAPTER 6
MINDFUL FLOW

...

PREFACE

Kathmandu Valley, October 1994

A group of fifty people from across the world had gathered for a ten-day beginners meditation retreat, located in a Tibetan monastery overlooking Kathmandu Valley, in the foothills of the Himalayan Mountains. I was lucky enough to be one of them, visiting Nepal for six months to teach English as a foreign language, between school and university.

The Gompa (Tibetan for meditation room) where the introduction to the retreat took place, was lit softly. A calmly spoken Buddhist nun with a slight Scandinavian accent said in a very gentle manner: 'Try and bring your attention to the sensation of your breathing, rest in the present moment.' As I sat on the floor, with a slight pain in one of my knees, my mind felt scattered, drifting into the future and the past. I tried to follow the instruction. From time to time, during the guided practice, I was reminded to return my attention to the breathing.

Gradually my mind started to find the thread of the breath, and I focused. I had a glimpse of concentration and clarity, a moment of peace. Immediately, I was hooked. As the session progressed, my eyes opened a little and surveyed the room. In the Gompa, everyone I could see appeared to be serene and calm.

As I was sitting there, thoughts and intentions flashed through my mind. This experience was something I wanted to have again, learn more about, and share with my friends and family back home. From this first trip to Nepal up to the present day, the intention to pass on mindful meditation practices has grown slowly and organically within my mind. Writing this book is an expression of this wish.

Mindful meditation has been practised extensively for over 2,500 years within the Buddhist tradition, and this book draws from the richness of this ancient lineage while presenting the practices in a purely secular form, suitable for all. My decision to write this book came from students requests who attend my live courses, workshops and retreats, wishing to have a book, so that they could continue with their learning and practice at home. Using my training, combined with feedback received from the community, I present to you the most comprehensive introduction to mindful meditation that I possibly can.

Teaching and writing do not necessarily indicate that I have any unique qualities or am an expert in the field. It merely provides me with the opportunity to develop, strengthen, and clarify the mindful training within my mind, while sharing these precious practices with those who wish to do the same. In this way, we learn and grow together. I am continually grateful for the opportunity to spend my life being able to do this. As the great Indian meditator Shantideva stated at the beginning of his Guide, written in the eighth century:

There is nothing here that has not been explained before
And I have no skill in the art of rhetoric;
Therefore, lacking any intention to benefit others,
I write this in order to acquaint it to my mind.

For due to acquaintance with what is wholesome,
The force of my faith may for a short while increase because of these words.
If, however, these words are seen by others
Equal in fortune to myself, it may be meaningful for them.'

This book was initially hand-written in two notebooks when I was in Copenhagen, New York, and London. Then it was transferred onto my computer, going through several edits and revisions in the UK and South East Asia. I printed one copy of the book, edited the copy again by hand and then updated the file. I passed the text to several editors who did a great job and made helpful suggestions on improvements. I continued to update and refresh the instructions, and practices, to make them as relevant, accessible and easy to apply, as possible.

This editing process has taken place while simultaneously teaching these eight themes (which correspond to the eight chapters), extensively in live classes and online, to thousands of people. Thus allowing me to present to you the most updated and relevant versions of these timeless, mindful practices. I sincerely hope you can benefit from reading and engaging with this book, and that these peaceful methods of training the mind, can reach countless people across the world, bringing peace into our lives and communities.

With very best wishes and a mindful heart
Adam Dacey
Bangkok,
August 2018

INTRODUCTION

The structure, content, and design of this book have arisen and evolved from over twenty years of continual teaching and study of these meditations. Practical methods to train the mind are introduced across eight main chapters, each beginning with the word 'Mindful'. Sections in which the reader is invited to take their time, and concentrate on the practice described, begin and end with a ❖.

Working gradually through the text, and engaging with the practices in the order presented, will lead to beneficial results. If you are taking a live or online class in conjunction with this book, then the content will strengthen and enrich your learning. By practising regularly, and engaging practically with the instructions, you will be able to develop a stable mental foundation within your mind, for a peaceful and happy life.

As you progress through the book, you will find each practice naturally leads to the next.

Following each of the five practices contained within the eight chapters is like taking a trip to eight countries around the world, and visiting five cities within each respective country. You can take as much time as you need to explore each city and country. You may enter one city where you want to relax for a while and enjoy the surroundings. In other locations, you may wish to fly through, perhaps to spend more time exploring the next time you visit.

I recommend working through this book, from one practice to the next, travelling from city to city, country to country. You may wish to jump ahead in your trip, but your journey will be more productive and in-depth if you choose to take time in each city and country, as mapped out in the text. In this way, you will progressively build your practice in the richest and most insightful manner.

At stages during the text, I refer to our life when we are at work. Please be aware that this does not only include paid employment. It can apply to charity work, voluntary work, and housework; whatever tasks you are engaged in, use the training creatively.

The practices are introduced to guide you gently into a mindful way of life. When we train the mind, we are taking an inner journey, thereby making each of the methods presented here inclusive for everyone, regardless of our external circumstances. I believe if you apply these instructions, you will develop the confidence to establish a mindful meditation practice within your daily life, and consequently enjoy all the significant benefits of this training.

Following in the footsteps of the great meditation masters from the past, you too can come to enjoy serenity and bliss within your mind, have a happy life and bring harmony to your world.

MINDFUL LISTENING

*Enjoying practices that naturally bring us
to the present moment while enhancing our
communication with the world*

Listen to the Breath

Gentle training to start our practice

The live beginner classes that I teach begin with a series of mindful listening practices. They help to establish a stable foundation for further training and draw us naturally into the present moment. We are all busy. Buddhist monks are busy; retired people often comment they are busier than when they worked full-time. Many of us would like to be able to meditate, step back and reflect, but it often feels, due to the busyness, there is just no time. Even when we finally sit down to practise or attend a class, we may feel that our mind is so distracted, it is almost impossible to enjoy a sense of calm and relaxation.

Perhaps we feel we cannot practise now due to the number of thoughts in our head, that it is too challenging for us at this time, or that we have approached meditation too late in our life. We are going to explore throughout this text how being busy does not need to prevent us from being mindful. Feeling that we do not have the time to practise may mean that our wish to train the mind is not yet strong enough. We can increase our wish to practise by reflecting on the significant benefits of training for both ourselves and others. We cultivate confidence by engaging in creative, simple and brief mindful meditations. Let us begin with a short, essential practice so that we can gain a subjective experience.

...

Watching Thoughts
Stepping back from the busyness

Take a few moments to slow down, pause, and bring your attention to the present moment.

Gradually start to watch your thoughts as they pass.

As though you were sitting on the side of a river, watching it flow.

Not expecting anything to happen.

Observe the movement of your thoughts for a short time.

...

Our thoughts tend to move towards potential activity in the future or something that has happened in the past. Just watching our thoughts in a relaxed way for a few moments each day will make a positive impression on our mind and start to provide us with an objective viewpoint for observing our life. We will look at this practice in more depth and detail when we engage in the mindful mind training in chapter four.

Generally, our thoughts take us away from the moment. So if we are sitting in a room, they can take us outside of the room, to activities we need to engage in and to problems that need solving. The practice of mindful listening helps us to meet our mind, wherever it may currently be. Gradually, gently and authentically, we bring our attention to the present moment.

Our distracted mind can be likened to a boat adrift at sea. In this training, we encourage our boat-like mind to the shore of the present moment. Mindful listening practice starts this process by using our sense of hearing to bring our mind to the here and now. Usually, we are distracted by the objects found by our senses. In this practice, instead of fighting with these distractions and applying tension to try and turn our mind in a new direction, we go to them. This approach will make our entrance into the world of meditation relaxed and natural.

If we check our mind, it is usually full of distractions, making it challenging to have any mental clarity. It can seem that the boat of our mind is too far out to sea to be able to bring it to the present moment. The practical way to encourage the boat of our mind into the now is to meet it, to go to it, then we will not need to force it to do anything. Trying to yank our mind impatiently into the present moment is ineffective and can lead to further distractions.

When we begin our training we need to be gentle with our mind. Go and meet the distracted mind where it is. To do this, we can listen to the sounds outside of where we are sitting. We let our mind go to the sounds and use them to remind us of the present moment. Whatever the sounds are, that is the sound of the present moment.

A helpful way to understand what it means to be mindful, is that it is to have a non-judgmental awareness of the present moment.

When we train in listening mindfully, we try to listen to the sounds around us, with an open, non-judgmental mind. We listen; we do not judge any of the sounds we hear or expect anything to happen. If we listen patiently, over time, we will naturally become mindful, and be able to abide peacefully.

Firstly, we listen to the sounds outside of the room or space where we are practising. Then we gradually draw our mind to the sounds we can hear within the room and then finally to the sounds within our body. Through this process, we gently guide the boat of our mind into the present moment. For absolute beginners, mindful listening is a relaxing, smooth way to commence their training. We gain an immediate, natural experience of being in the present moment.

Without rushing, succumbing to frustration, or being too concerned with what the sounds we hear are, we listen mindfully. In this way, we start to establish a foundation for subsequent mindful practices. Try this brief mindful listening practice

.

...

One Minute Practice

Getting started

Listen to all the sounds around you.

Mindfully open your awareness to what you can hear.

Pause everything other than listening.

Try to sit quietly and still.

If you have any thoughts about the past or the future, let them pass through your mind.

Allow any sounds that you hear to bring you into the present moment.

...

When we engage in any mindful practice, it is helpful to appreciate that as well as practising for the person who we are now, we are also sowing seeds for future peaceful experiences. When a gardener plants seeds they wait for them to grow, in the knowledge that they will ripen in their own time; so with our practice, we take a relaxed step back and allow it to mature naturally, in its own time. Appreciating this helps us to have a relaxed approach to our training, and means we are making a significant investment in the mental health of our future self. We will come to experience all the beneficial effects of our practice.

We can have a calm connection with our practice if we appreciate that mindful meditation is the cause of inner peace. Through not expecting immediate results and having confidence in the methods, our mind will naturally open and relax. When we create the causes of inner peace, the effects will ripen naturally in their own time.

...

Throughout the book, there will be explanations of many different practices, some we can engage in when we are on the move, for others it is good to sit somewhere quietly and take a little time out, to give our self the chance to focus, unwind and enjoy our mind. For quiet practice, here are a few tips to get started:

- Try to sit in a comfortable, grounded posture.
- If you are practising at home, choose an area that you can sit in regularly each day so that space starts to become your personal, mindful zendo (a place set aside within the Zen temples of Japan for meditation).
- If you are sitting on a chair, make sure your feet are on the floor, with your shoulders loose, and your back relatively straight, while at the same time relaxed and not too tense.

- If you are sitting on the floor, whether that be cross-legged or kneeling, make sure that you have a firm base, by ensuring that you have enough cushions beneath you. Initially practising on the floor may be uncomfortable if you are not used to this way of sitting.
- Over time, if you wish, with familiarity you can start to build up the strength in your body, finding this position suitable for practice, feeling comfortable and relaxed when you sit down to be mindful.
- Allow your eyes to close gently. If you feel tired keep them slightly open.
- Tilt your head down, just a little bit.
- Allow your hands to relax in your lap or on your legs.

The essential point of finding a relaxed posture is to be able to sit in a position that is comfortable enough, so while staying awake and alert, you can almost forget about your body.

...

When we are practising mindful meditation, we need to be aware of our mind when it gets overexcited due to distractions, and when it becomes dull and starts to fall asleep. Excitement and mental dullness take our attention away from the present moment and have a significant part to play in the stress and anxiety that arises in our life.

We need to be on the lookout for these two factors when we practice. We are not pushing them away or battling with them; we are adopting a more skilful approach. We learn to invite distractions into our mind so that we can see them, but we do not go as far as entertaining them. In the Zen texts they say we invite thoughts into our mind, but we do not serve them tea.

...

With mindful listening we are focusing on the sounds that we hear, not our inner conversation. When we start to become aware of the sounds around us, whatever they may be, this process helps us to go of the thoughts in our mind, and brings us into the moment. The sounds around us may seem as though they are distractions. Here, with skilful practice, we are transforming them into our mindful training.

...

Single-Pointed Concentration
Establish a quality of focus

In this book, you will hear the expression single-pointed concentration. Understanding the meaning can help to improve the quality of our mindful practice. There are many different types of concentration. 'Single-pointed' is when we focus and exclusively rest the mind on a specific object of meditation. For example, with the breath, we first locate the sensation and then focus single-pointedly. All that is arising in our consciousness is the breath. Training in single-pointed concentration will help to naturally sharpen the clarity in our mind and bring peace into our life.

We may find that when we try to concentrate single-pointedly, although there is some focus, the mind is also thinking about other things. Making it double-pointed, triple-pointed, even quadruple-pointed. We can be observing the breathing, while half-thinking about something else we need to do later. Perhaps this feels natural, as we are so used to multitasking.

Our mind may not be familiar with being single-pointed, however, we have the potential and ability to cultivate this skill. We do

8

not need to force our mind. We just patiently keep bringing our attention to our object of meditation, in this instance the breathing, connecting with its sensation. With training, our mind will naturally start to focus. Boredom may initially arise. This is not a bad sign. The mind is not used to moving in a different direction to distraction. Be patient, meditate regularly, and our ability to be single-pointed will grow.

If, during our daily activities, we try to focus on one thing at a time – single tasking – this can also help when we come to train in single-pointed concentration, as our mind is already relatively focused.

...

Here is a more extended practice, to help clarify the meaning of mindful listening and gain an experiential understanding.

...

Mindful Listening Practice
Gain a practical experience

Begin by gently and slowly reading.

For a profound practice, gradually learn and memorise, so you can mentally recite to yourself with your eyes closed.

If you engage with this training regularly, it will start to flow and feel natural.

Settle into a comfortable posture. Allow your eyes to rest closed and your face to relax.

Feel the sensation of your body against the floor. Whether that is the soles of your feet, if you are sitting on a chair, or your legs and knees if you are sitting on the floor.

Listen to the sounds outside of the room or space where you are practising.

Use your awareness of the sounds to bring your attention into the present moment.

Whatever the sounds are, listen with an open and attentive mind.

When your thoughts take you outside of the room to distractions, use the sounds that you hear to bring your awareness into the present. Spend a short time just listening and following the sounds outside.

Then begin to notice the sounds inside the room that you are in, the hum of the room. Listen with an open ear and draw yourself into the present moment.

Gradually gather your mind inside your body.

Start noticing and listening to the sounds within the body.

In particular, try to become aware of the sound of your breathing.

Can you hear the subtle, natural sound of the breath?

Use the awareness of the sounds of your breath, to draw you into the present.

Try to listen single-pointedly, in a relaxed, focused way.

If your mind becomes distracted, then use the sounds of the breath to bring you into the present moment.

If your mind wanders to sounds outside the room, go to the sounds, relax and refocus, then gradually draw your attention inwards.

Start to notice the sound within the room, and then the sound of your breath inside the body.

Without too much tension or strain, try to abide mindfully with the sound of your breath, listening for as long as possible.

Follow this process throughout the duration of your session.

As your mind goes out to distractions, try to notice the drifting. Start to become aware of the sounds around you, then inside the room, and then inside your body.

Try to rest in each moment for as long as you feel comfortable.

Just before you finish listening mindfully, dedicate your practice so you can progress with the training and it can be of benefit to all those around you.

❖

...

Some people like to document their mindful practices in a journal or diary so that they can see their progress. This habit may be something that works for you.

...

Everyone appreciates a good listener. Listening well improves our relationships both at home and work, strengthening our memory and focus, naturally drawing others to us, helping them to feel comfortable and relaxed in our presence. When talking to others, distractions can take us away from the conversation. The mindful practices presented in this first chapter can help improve the way in which we listen so that we can offer those in our life our full presence. The greatest present we can offer someone is our presence. We will look more directly at this skill in the final practice of this chapter, Listening to a Friend, on page twenty.

...

In mindful training, we are learning how to do one thing at a time; in this instance, just listening. We gently guide our mind away from the stress of distractions. So when we listen, we just listen. We let all the other mental activity and distraction pass.

...

Listen to Nature

Enhancing mindfulness in the great outdoors

We can see the effects of urbanisation across the world, with more of us moving to the city and away from nature. If we take the time to venture into nature, we can appreciate the stark contrast between the busyness of the city, and the calm which a natural environment exudes, resulting in our mind unwinding and slowing down.

The Japanese talk about 'Shinrin Yoku', which translates as 'forest bathing' and is actively encouraged for those children who reside in Tokyo, and other cities across Japan, as a way to help them reduce stress and anxiety in their lives. Nature has a peaceful effect on our body and mind, bringing power and presence to our mindfulness training. Our mind pacifies in nature; we breathe deeper, feel less rushed, and can naturally settle more into the moment.

If we live in an urban environment and we do not have the time to go deep into the countryside, we can retreat somewhere with a little nature; into the garden, the park, or by the canal or river that runs through our city. In the listening to nature practice, we go alone, or with a friend who is going to share the experience with us. I firstly recommend trying this practice while sitting down outside, quietly in nature. We can also do this training while we are walking (visit chapter five for more information on mindful walking in nature).

Set a precise amount of time to engage with the listening training. Decide at the beginning of your practice that during this time, you are not going to do anything other than to listen mindfully while letting your distracting thoughts pass.

...

❖

Go outside into nature and, in your chosen spot, begin to draw your attention into the body, gathering your mind to the present moment.

Start to listen to the sounds around you. Open your ears to the sound of nature, in a mindful, non-judgmental manner.

Settle into the moment and try to listen openly.

If you hear a bird tweeting, instead of latching onto what you are hearing and thinking, 'what type of bird is this', just listen to its sound, let it arise and dissolve, patiently listen and calmly let the sound pass.

You may hear the wind rustling through the leaves; let it guide you into the present moment.

Whatever sounds come, mentally step back and allow yourself to become mindful.

As time passes, you may wish to take your practice deeper, and reflect: 'Where does the sound come from; where does it go?'

With this contemplation, let yourself travel deeper into the sound.

In this mindful space, practise patiently for the time you have set yourself.

It is natural to become distracted; allow your mind to relax, let any busy thoughts pass. Use the sounds of nature to bring your attention to each moment.

Just before your practice concludes, decide to maintain your mindful awareness in daily life, by being attentive to the sounds around you, and letting them assist in bringing you to the present moment.

Make the intention to continue practising for the benefit of all those in your life and society.

...

Listening to nature has a soporific effect on our consciousness. Most of our distractions and worries come from either thinking about future events or what has happened in the past. Mindfully listening helps to initiate the habit of bringing our mind and self into the present moment.

...

Listen to the City

In the middle of distraction come to
enjoy an urban stillness

This practice is slightly more challenging and can help us if we work or live in a busy environment. The sounds of the city are numerous: traffic, talking, music, the hubbub of conversation, extractor fans, and sirens. When we walk through the city, we tend to be heading somewhere, on a mission, our mind partially in the future or past. Even if we stop and take a coffee or pause for lunch, our mind is still moving, rushing; distracting us by looking at our phone, reading a book or a newspaper.

In this training, although we are in the middle of busyness, we stop and listen. Why would we listen to the city? These are the sounds around us right now, the sounds of the present moment, and through listening to them, whatever they are, we can draw our attention into the here and now, tapping into the world of mindfulness.

You are going to stop in the city, maybe in your office, on a bench, perhaps in a cafe.

Either gently rest your eyes, or keep them slightly open.

Just abide for a short time and do nothing other than listen to the sounds around you.

Use the sounds as hooks to bring you fully into the present.

Open your ears mindfully to the sound.

Allow whatever sounds arise to bring you into the present moment.

Abide within the concrete jungle, bringing your attention inside.

Whatever the sounds are, you do not need to label them as good or bad, all you need to do is mindfully open your ears with a non-judgmental awareness.

Gradually allow the sounds to guide your mind into the present moment.

Practise this training for as long as you are comfortable, perhaps a few minutes, or longer if you have time, and you will start to get into the flow of the training.

When you are ready to bring the practice to conclusion, make the determination to try and abide within the present moment during the rest of your day.

...

We can incorporate this practice into our daily life. Maybe we are sitting on a train, tram, or bus; pause for a few moments and listen to the sounds. Whatever they are, listen in such a way so that the sounds draw you into the present moment. Let thoughts of the future and past pacify and subside. Remember the understanding of mindfulness that I introduced at the beginning of the text; a non-judgmental awareness of the present moment. As we listen, we apply this awareness.

Developing the ability to listen mindfully is a training of the mind and takes time. Like learning any new skill or discipline, if we can practise regularly, our ability grows. The mindful practices presented in this text come from a minimal 'less is more' approach. As we train, we do not need to add or impose anything to the practice. With mindful listening, we open our awareness to the sounds around us. Keep your mindful training simple, and you will come to enjoy all the beneficial effects.

Sometimes I am asked in the live classes that I teach, the difference between daydreaming and mindful meditation. Daydreaming is where we have trains of thought, streams of consciousness, and we follow them. Depending on the thoughts and which way they go, this can be quite relaxing. When we daydream and follow a stream of conceptual thought, our mind can go from the present moment into the world of distraction.

Mindful training is different. With respect to mindful listening, we are not following streams of thought about the sounds we hear. We are using the sounds to bring us to the moment, and thereby encourage our self to be present. We start to enjoy a natural way of letting go of the stress and anxiety that arise from worrying about the past and future. The ability to relax and abide in the present moment comes from having continuously trained our mind. Wherever we are in our life, right now, we can start to establish and learn this extremely beneficial mindful habit.

Through the course of this book, I will share many mindfulness practices. Mindful listening training is an excellent way to get started and will lay the foundation for subsequent practices. It is for this reason that I always begin my introductory courses with this theme.

...

Listen to Music

Increasing focus while deepening our
appreciation of music

Music is everywhere, in shops, cafes, supermarkets, hospitals, and taxis; whenever we are out-and-about in public life, there is usually music playing. We can have music on, almost continuously, in the background of our lives, as a soundtrack to our entire existence. In today's world, music is easy to access, and if we are not immediately happy with a song, a new track is just one click, one moment, away. We can become so accustomed to having sound in the background that not having music, the radio, or television on, can seem a little strange, or boring, and make our interaction with life feel dry. If we check carefully, however, this response is due to a habit of mind; a mental tendency.

I went into a cafe in London's Brick Lane, one lazy Sunday afternoon, and as I entered I said to the barista working behind the counter, 'It is nice and quiet in here'. Laughing slightly nervously, she said, 'Oh, yes don't worry, we're going to put some music on now'. Ten-seconds later, music was blaring out of the speakers.

Let us reflect:-how often when we hear music, do we listen to it completely? Practising musicians definitely will. Perhaps music connoisseurs attending a concert may follow the course of a piece of music. Unless it is our work, we may only give the music we hear some of our attention. With mindful training, we are starting to give the sounds that arise in our life our full attention.

Music can so quickly be a tool that makes our mind drift off to past events of nostalgia or future events that are yet to come. We can cultivate a habit of mind to the point that, when we hear music, we will either drift off or it just fades into the background. Here, with this practice of mindful listening to music, we play a piece of music and engage with it single-pointedly, like with the above practice of listening to nature and the city, we use the activity of listening to bring us into the present moment.

You can do this practice sitting in the meditation posture, sitting in a chair, or lying down.

Usually, I recommend a simple piece of slow, classical, piano music, or a track with one or two instruments, not too elaborate; perhaps, relaxing, ambient music. When you first start this practice, also ensure that the music is instrumental, with no lyrics to distract your thoughts.

Please take note of how long the music will last, before you begin, and decide to stay focused and concentrated through its duration.

Press play and try to follow the shapes of the music.

Use the sound of the music to bring yourself into the present moment. Follow its flow and listen carefully.

Note each beat and rhythm and allow your mind to move along with each sound.

Let the different feelings, thoughts and memories, that the music conjures up, come and go. Use the sounds to bring you into the present.

We mindfully marvel in the magic of the sound, without drifting off.

As your practice deepens you can reflect:

Where does the sound come from; where does it go?'

When the music ends, determine to take a mindful awareness into the rest of your day and life.

...

Making this determination at the end of our training will give our practice impetus and drive. Over time, many people we come into contact with will benefit. The practice of mindful listening not only helps us to train in being mindful in general but also enhances our enjoyment of music, taking us deeper and allowing a greater appreciation of the sounds we hear. As I progressed with this practice, I started to use music less as background sound in my day-to-day activity and became happier with sometimes having just the sound of silence.

...

Listen to a Friend

Enhancing our mindful communication

Sometimes conversations can be two people talking, with breaks in between. Mindful listening can turn our conversations into an art, helping us to be more engaged, and the channel of communication to become more profound and fulfilling. The quality of our relationships depends upon the quality of our listening. Relationships at work and home can break down when our listening fades. If we listen mindfully to someone, with an open, non-judgmental mind, then the person we are listening to can relax and feel more comfortable.

It is often challenging to listen when our mind is busy. We can be so edgy, waiting for a gap in the conversation to express what we are going to say next, that it is difficult to listen mindfully. If we listen completely, we can hear much more than the words and appreciate the point of view of the speaker.

This next practice, listening to a friend, provides us with the opportunity to do this.

...

❖

You need to do this practice with another person, taking it in turns to be the speaker and the listener. The session has three parts and takes six minutes to complete.

Firstly, the speaker talks for two minutes about what they have been doing that day. It is not so much about what the speaker is saying but more what the listener is doing with their mind.

The listener sits, abiding in the present moment, just listening to the speaker. They can occasionally nod if they feel the need to acknowledge. The listener does not say anything or engage in conversation, they mindfully listen.

As the listener, you attend to what is being said, following the sentences and noting the sounds of the words. Enjoy the opportunity to listen to the speaker.

It can be enlightening when you first do this training, after a minute, or so, you become relaxed and less self-conscious of listening.

This training will help you to focus single-pointedly when you are having a conversation and not habitually drift off, thereby enhancing your relationships at work and home.

Secondly, after two minutes, the speaker and listener swap roles. The listener becomes the speaker, and the speaker becomes the listener. Then for another two minutes engage in the same practice. Be mindful of the words coming from the speaker.

Thirdly, for the final two minutes, chat with each other about the practice of listening. What was it like to listen completely? What did you notice?

How do you think this practice could help your relationships?

...

In this first chapter, we have engaged in a series of practices to grow our ability to listen mindfully, thus building a stable foundation for the subsequent training presented through the course of this book. Some final points, in conclusion from our exploration of mindful listening.

- Mindful listening is a practice that we can enjoy with our eyes open or closed.

- We can practise in both busy and quiet locations.

- Mindful listening practice can improve our relationships, enhance our appreciation of music, help us to connect more with our surroundings both in the city and the country, and start to strengthen our memory and focus.

- Mindful listening gathers and concentrates our mind, which helps us to be present and focused, allowing our engagement with life to be more satisfying.

- When we listen attentively, our mind will be less mixed with the filter of our discrimination. The interactions we enjoy are enhanced by having less distraction and judgment.

- Developing the ability to listen with an open, accepting and far-reaching mind, provides a foundation for our mindful training, where we can abide moment by moment, with non-judgmental awareness.

- With mindful listening, we transform our sense of hearing, which can so easily distract us, into a tool that will help to focus the mind and bring us into the present moment.

- Mindful listening is an art that we can train in and develop over the course of time.

If we gently reflect on these benefits, we will have enthusiasm and positive energy to engage with this practice continually.

MINDFUL BODY

How to abide in the present moment

In this set of practices, we are using an awareness of our body to draw us into the present moment, away from distractions and worry. If we check carefully, when anxiety and worry arises, it is usually from mulling over something that could happen in the future, or from being preoccupied with something that happened in the past. Many worries we have about future events never manifest; although they take up much of our mind space, they never occur.

Training in being mindful naturally guides our attention into the present. We learn to fully accept in each moment what is happening both around and inside of us. Abiding in the present moment provides us with an opportunity to let go of the future and the past. Having a skilful, mindful awareness of our body can help us to become fully present and live a meaningful life.

If we observe our mental habits, as human beings, we tend to be continuously conscious of our body, making sure that it is okay, well fed and watered, looking good and youthful! Much of the time this awareness of the body does not lead to good results and can generate heightened sensitivity, resulting in anguish and worry.

However, if we train in the mindful body practices, developing an awareness of our body, which is non-judgmental and open, then the relationship we have with it can become more positive and lead to peace. Through training in the practices contained within this chapter, we will make this possible.

Our body is always in the present moment; let us now briefly reflect on this so we can gain a deeper understanding.

...

Gradually start to become aware of your body.

It is here. Gently notice it.

Feel the sensation of your body against the chair or floor.

Wiggle your toes a few times.

Take several mindful breaths.

Notice all the sensations of your breath and the effect that it has, as it travels around your body.

...

Our mind does connect with our body, but some of the time it can be partially separated. Our body can be in a room, but our mind is outside, thinking of other events. We can be walking along the street, but completely unaware of our body and its movement. We can eat a delicious meal and not be aware of our posture and the subtle sensations in our body. For much of the time, our body is just a vehicle transporting us around our life, needing regular servicing and maintenance. Our intimate relationship with it requires us to expend much attention and energy.

In some traditions of meditation, they say that the body is like a temple. The body is something sacred. With mindful body training, we are not saying or imputing anything upon the body; we are just becoming aware of it in a non-judgmental, open and accepting way. As a result of having this perspective, we can start to move away from distractions and open a rich doorway to the present moment.

...

To help you have a clear mind and allow your practice to progress, before starting your session, decide on a timescale. Just like a good story, when you train in mindful practice, be clear when your training begins, when you are in the middle of it, and when it ends. Try also to start all your mindful practices with a positive intention, increasing your focus as you progress and concluding with a dedication when the session ends. Read the practice sections which start and finish with a ❖, slowly and mindfully.

...

Mindful Hands: Sitting & Standing

Relaxing meditations to bring
instant stress relief and calm

...

Mindful Hands

Sitting

Sit in a relaxed, comfortable posture and gather your attention into the present moment.

Start to notice where you are, by listening to the sounds around you.

Let these sounds start to gather your attention inwards.

Gradually become aware of your body.

Notice the contact between your body and the floor, or chair.

Become aware of the sensations in your body. Notice whatever they are, maybe a tingling in the back, a sense of cold or warmth.

Use the sensations to bring your attention into the present moment.

Try to become aware of your body.

Allow the awareness of your body to ground you into the present moment.

Your body is an anchor for the ship of your mind.

Feel its weight.

Notice the bones, the hardness.

Gather all your attention inside, and try to let go of the distractions that take you to the outside world.

Draw your attention inwards.

Place both hands on your stomach, with your left gently rested on the right.

Start to become aware of your hands.

Notice their movement, as they rise and fall in time with your breath.

Use this movement as your point of focus for the rest of the practice.

Be aware of the rising and falling of your hands, nothing else. Appreciating this is the natural movement of your calm body.

The awareness of this movement draws you into the body, away from distractions, and unites your attention with the breathing.

Stay with this for as long as possible.

When your attention wanders, gently bring it back to your hands and the movement of your breath.

You are beginning the process of uniting your body and mind, developing an awareness of your body that brings peace and calm.

Gently, bring your attention to this sensation and movement throughout the duration of your session.

Just abide in the present, following one moment to the next. We start to go deeper and beyond the surface level stress, letting a relaxation and calmness arise.

Abide with this process for as long as you wish.

As your session ends, dedicate the energy from your training so that you can progress with the practice and it can benefit everyone in your life.

Try to incorporate this practice into elements of your daily life, and you will start to enjoy the far-reaching effects of mindful training. For example, when you are sitting in the office and need a little mindful energy to reduce the stress from your mind and feel more grounded, you can do a short version of this practice. You do not need to close your eyes; use the awareness of your body to gather your mind. The environment may be noisy and distracting, but you can enjoy tapping into the present moment with this short practice. Place your hand on your stomach and feel the rising and falling of your breath, just for a few moments.

With a dynamic, flexible approach, you can do this training in your office, while you are waiting for a train or before you go to bed, while you are waiting for a programme on the television. I know someone who even used this training to significant effect, to help themselves find release from anxiety while lying on a hospital operating table waiting for the surgeon.

When you have gained some experience of this practice, you can begin to notice the rising and falling of your body against your clothes, without the need to place your hands on your stomach.

...

Try now, just for a few moments, to notice the natural movement (due to the breathing) of your stomach and chest against your clothes. Pause and become aware. Slow down your world, and abide within the moment.

...

With creativity and enthusiasm, many opportunities to practice during the day will present themselves. We can start to integrate a mindful awareness into our everyday activities, and thereby gain stable confidence in the power of our practice to effect positive change in our life. Now we can explore how to train in the mindful hands practice when we are standing up.

...

Mindful Hands

Standing

Stand with both your feet flat on the floor, level with your shoulders.

Bend your legs slightly, so you feel grounded and rooted to the floor.

Place your left hand on your right against the navel.

Have a straight but relaxed back, allowing your shoulders to rest.

Draw your attention inside the body.

Take a few mindful breaths, gathering your attention within.

Notice the feeling of the floor underneath your body; bring your attention to the rising and falling of your hands on your stomach.

Gently and gradually bring yourself to the present moment.

Stand, abiding in this position for a few minutes.

Whenever your mind wanders to distraction, use the awareness of your body to bring you to the present moment.

Just before finishing the practice, determine to carry your awareness into the rest of the day.

...

Each day we spend time standing, whether it's for a few moments in a queue, at the traffic lights, or standing on public transport. Even if it's just for a few seconds, take the opportunity during these moments to practise mindful standing. Draw your attention to the present moment, noticing your posture. Become aware of where you are.

Life today can be quite sedentary, and much of the time we can be static, with screen-time hours taking up much of our life. Even if we have to stand for a short time, it is not long before we are quickly looking for a place to sit down. When, due to our circumstances, we are forced to stand, it is rare to stand with presence, independently. We tend to lean or compensate our weight on one side of the body. Thus, our mind becomes distracted.

Becoming mindful when we are standing helps to tap into the present moment during the day. We connect with the present, which then gives us a much-needed boost of energy. Mindful standing can be a helpful doorway into the present moment for those who find it difficult to make the time to sit. When you gain experience of mindful standing, you will be able to approach the moments that you stand in a completely different way.

Standing is no longer a chore. Less a time when we become distracted and feel the need to get our phone out again, and more a time when we can be aware, enjoying being present. Standing becomes an opportunity to tap into our mindfulness practice and recharge.

When you are next in the supermarket why not look out for the long queue! It will provide the time and space to practise mindful standing. Gradually we can start to transform the process of waiting, and just like that, the time to practise mindfulness appears in many places throughout our life.

The mindful sitting and standing practices require little conceptual thought; they help to focus our attention on the sensations in our body, resulting in the pacification of the busyness within.

Now let us explore a practice which strengthens our ability to focus and relax while letting go of our physical pain.

...

Mindful Body Scan

Take your time, training the mind to
focus and release tension

If you wish to extract the most out of the mindful body scan I recommend giving yourself quality time to enjoy this training; at least twenty-five minutes. This practice can be done either sitting in the meditation posture, on the floor or a chair, or lying down, on a mat, on a couch, on your bed, or even on the beach. If you practise lying down, be aware of the distracted mind, and also becoming drowsy and slipping into a state of sleep.

For a meditator, there are two main obstacles:

1. Mental sinking, when dullness strikes, and we drift into sleep.
2. Mental excitement, when our mind is full of distractions.

When we are lying down it is essential to practise alertness, so we are aware of the mind that wishes to drift into sleep. We allow our mind to become more relaxed, subtle and absorbed, but not to become distracted and drowsy. For instructions on improving sleep, refer to chapter seven. To engage in the mindful body scan, try to follow the words below and gradually memorise.

...

Settle into a comfortable position and place both hands on your stomach. Let them relax and loosen. Place your left hand on your right at the level of your navel.

Set your intention: *'I am going to train in this practice so that I can bring mindfulness into my life and so my friends and family can also benefit from my development of mental peace.'*

Gather your attention into your body.

Become aware of your hands and the movement they make in time with your breathing.

Connect with your body. Connect with the present moment.

Bring your full awareness gently to the crown of your head.

Try to focus on your crown, and notice any sensations; with your mind, gradually explore this area.

As your mind moves to the crown of your head, let the area relax.

Move your awareness around the body noticing and relaxing the areas that it meets.

Scanning, abiding, and relaxing.

Bring your attention to your forehead, notice the area, and gradually scan across, from one side to the other.

Become aware of the sensations. Notice and let go.

Gradually become aware of your eyes and allow them to relax.

Notice your face and jaw.

Your face may be holding onto tension; become aware of this, let it go, allow your face to drop and relax as you become aware.

Notice and focus on the top of your neck. Bring your attention within and start to allow the top of your back to relax, just by gently placing your awareness here.

Mentally explore the area around the top of your spine and let it relax.

Take a broad awareness of your head and hold your attention here for a short time.

Bring your attention to your neck and shoulders. Let your shoulders gently drop and loosen.

Identify any areas of tension, and let them dissolve as you gently focus.

Become aware of your arms. Mentally follow down from your shoulders to your hands, then along to your fingertips.

What sensations do you notice?

Bring your awareness to the movement of your hands in time with your breathing.

Spend a short time focusing on this movement, drawing all your attention to the process.

Come to the top of your spine.

Scan down your spine, becoming aware of all the different sensations, letting go of any stress and tension that has built up.

Along the spine, you may find knots of tension. Start to breathe into them.

Identify the knot, place your concentration on and around the area, breathe into it and allow the knot to unravel gradually.

Scan down your back, working all the way down to the base, scanning gently, calmly letting go.

Once you have reached the base of your spine, take a general awareness of your back and the sensations which are arising.

Start to explore the front of your body, gradually drawing your attention within.

Become aware of your chest, go deep into the body and notice how your internal organs move in time with your breathing.

Notice how your breath descends into your body and nourishes all your organs.

Feel the sensation of your breath in your throat and notice how it moves your lungs.

Scanning gently around your body become aware of your heart, recognising how it nourishes your organs.

Start to notice your stomach. There may be stress and tension here; become aware of this, allow it to loosen, and let your breath heal it.

As you gently explore the stomach, let any tension and tightness unravel.

Come to your hands again, notice their movement on your stomach, stay with this rising and falling for a short time.

Then come to your legs, scan down to your feet, toes, and the soles of your feet.

Abide, mindfully, at the foot of your body.

If there is any tension left, let it descend and dissolve out through the soles of your feet.

Stay here for a short time. Then bring your awareness into the centre of your body.

Abide here.

Allow all your awareness to dissolve into the body.

Then scan up your back again, slowly ascending your spine, up to your neck and then to the crown of your head, keep your attention located here for a short time.

Then come to your hands again, and notice their movement in time with the breath. We are going to rest all our relaxed attention here for the remainder of the session.

Abide here, observing the rising and falling, until you are ready to conclude the session.

Just before you finish, dedicate all the good energy you have created, so that you can continue with your training, and all the people in your life can benefit from your practice.

...

This training is one of the most calming mindful practices presented in the text, helping us to physically and mentally unwind, and enjoy relaxation and stress relief. See the mindful night practice in chapter seven for another version of this training which encourages sleep. Review the calm sleep practice, also in chapter seven, for a version of this training which works well with children, helping them to unwind and let go of their day before sleep.

...

When we train in meditation, we will develop and increase the confidence that we have in the power of our mind. We are starting to look within, for the solution to our problems. When we experience a difficulty, we turn our attention inward, investigate and see if there is anything we can change in our mind, before we attempt to improve the external situation.

We live in a materialistic world, and one of the characteristics of this is that, when difficulties arise, we tend to seek something material outside of us to resolve the issue. This process can temporarily pacify our stress, but can also be frustrating as it does not get to the root of our anxiety, potentially creating new problems and issues we have to work through.

The root of our difficulties comes from the mind and how we respond to a situation. Material distractions can lead us away from getting to the cause of the issue. For example, when we have an issue with our body, it is normal to turn to a medical doctor and medicine to solve the problem. Sometimes this approach works, but perhaps the issue persists or reoccurs later.

If you ask any GP, they will tell you that 75-80% of those who attend their clinics are coming with stress-related disorders. The origin of much of the physical disease we endure in today's world comes from the stress within our mind. If we learn to change the mind we can harness its power and start to heal the body naturally. In the next practice, we are going to use our mindful attention to help reduce the pain in our body and gradually start to discover the healing power of mindfulness.

...

Mindful Pain Relief

Utilising the power of our mind to heal the body

This practice can be used to help us overcome pain and aches in our body. Be patient with the training. We cannot necessarily expect the results of the practice to be as immediate as a painkiller, but if we apply the methods consistently over time, then we will create the causes to witness the beneficial effects of our mindful training in the future. We start to generate the tendency to first turn to the mind when physical pain arises.

Sit in a comfortable, relaxed posture. Listen mindfully to the sounds around you.

Draw your attention within, becoming aware of your body and the sensations that pass through.

If your mind is distracted, place your hands on your stomach to connect with the movement of the breath.

Scan gently around the body, checking for any aches or pains.

If you have a sharp pain in one part of your body, try not to go there first, choose another area to begin with and gradually work your way to the more painful areas later.

Note the area of pain, mentally examine the location and take your mind right to the centre of where it is. Place your attention there for a short time.

Draw your breath gently to this area.

Calmly and carefully direct your breath to the location, abide there, and breathe into it.

Direct your breath to the pain and as you breathe out, let the pain dissolve and melt away.

Try not to expect immediate results, gradually follow the process.

Try again to breathe into the area, allow your breath to heal the pain gently.

After doing this for some time in one area, go to another location where there may be pain or tension.

Please do the same, breathe gently and deeply into it, and allow the pain to pacify and dissolve away.

The most important part of this training is to approach the exercise in a relaxed manner, slowly allowing your body and mind to unwind.

You can focus on taking several specific locations in your body, or you can do a general pain relief practice.

You will start to notice that when the mind begins to relax and unwind, the tension and pain in the body naturally releases.

...

If during the day you feel pain arising in your body, pause, bring your attention inward, and ask yourself exactly where the pain is. Take your mind to the area of pain, locate it, then gently breathe right into its centre. As you take a mindful breath, allow yourself to relax and let go. Engage with this mindful exercise as many times as you can.

...

All the practices presented in this book can help us to become more mindful. As time passes, more research is being conducted revealing the definite benefits of training in mindful meditation practice. However, no amount of research is going to give us an actual authentic experience and help us enjoy all the benefits of the training. Gaining insight comes through gradually establishing the mindful habit in our lives. We try not to expect too much, too soon, from the practice by looking for instant results. If we can remain happy while establishing this beneficial habit, then our mind will be relaxed and open. Even if we can only practise for a short time each day, we are creating causes for future effects.

Consider a gardener who is sowing seeds. When the conditions are right for the seeds to sprout, they will, but in their own time. We follow the same principle with our mindful practice. Focus on creating the causes, by engaging in the methods; eventually, all the benefits of mindful practice will ripen. With many of the mindful instructions presented in this book, we merely observe what is happening in the present moment. This approach does not require force; it just depends on us letting go and allowing the skin of our stress to shed.

...

In the next mindful body practice, we will observe the sensation of our breath in the body while using a very simple but effective visualisation used in the Tibetan meditative tradition.

...

Clear Body

————

Introducing a simple, helpful visualisation

Sit in a comfortable, upright, but relaxed posture.

Listen gently to the sounds around you.

Gather your mind and begin listening to the sounds within.

Notice the sensations in your body and the points of contact with the floor.

If you feel distracted, bring your hands to your stomach.
Observe how your hands move in time with your breathing.

Start to imagine all your pain, stress and negativity, gathering in the aspect of a dark cloud of smoke at the centre of your body.

As you breathe out, imagine letting go of this dark cloud.

Enjoy the moment as it disappears far into the distance.

Spend a short time engaging with this visualisation.

Start to notice your in-breath, imagine breathing in clear light, which brings clarity and healing into your body.

Spend a short time breathing in light and breathing out dark clouds of smoke.

Make sure to combine the breathing and visualisation, with your natural breath.

Imagine, as you breathe out, that you let go of the dark clouds far into the distance and, as you breathe in, you enjoy the clear light.

Breathe in clear light imagining that it heals your inner body.

Take your time.

As you breathe in, gently imagine your inner body becoming clear.

Visualise breathing in a pure, clear light which fills your entire body with clarity, and believe that your body is starting to heal.

Focus on this clear body for a short time, and enjoy each moment.

If there are distractions, negativity or pain in the body, patiently, release them, as you breathe out.

Guide your mind towards the clear body visualisations, mixing them with your natural breath.

Practise for as long as you can, in a relaxed manner, not pushing; enjoy the process.

Just before you finish the session, dedicate the fruits of your training so that it benefits everyone in your life and across the world.

If we can retain our focus, by introducing this simple, but very useful, clear body visualisation we can bring power to our meditation.

...

Mindful Anchor

———

Learning to ground ourselves into the present moment

Our distracted mind is like a ship sailing into the ocean of confusion and stress. We need an anchor to keep our mind present if we wish to train and progress with our practice. That is not to say there is never a time for the mind to be distracted, or that this training is anti-daydreaming. It is just encouraging us at points during the day to engage in a mental exercise that will strengthen the muscle of our mindfulness, thereby increasing our ability to be in the moment.

When the ship of our mind sails off into the sea of distractions, it can stay there for a long time. Possibly from the moment we wake, to the moment we fall asleep. Some days our mind is in a state of semi-distraction virtually all the time. One important element of mindful training is learning to focus on one thing at a time, keeping a single-pointed concentration, not obscured by distraction. To help our mindful journey progress let's explore how to anchor our self in the present moment.

In the mindful anchor training, we use our body to keep us present. We enter each new moment through the awareness of our body. The fact our human body is appearing to the mind, and we are breathing and alive, can remind us of the moment. Just like our body, the present is changing moment by moment. We cannot point to a moment and say here it is. Although we can take a still life photo portrait that snaps a moment in time, immediately after we have made the picture, the moment has gone.

If we were to sit in front of the mirror and wait to see changes in the appearance of our reflection, we would not see anything taking place. Even though change is happening, the increments are too subtle for our mind. We can only see changes over a more extended period.

To tune into the present moment, we need to keep refocusing and anchoring the mind, thus connecting with each new moment. What tends to happen is that our mind loses focus and drifts away. In this mindful anchor practice, we are learning to ground and keep our mind in the here and now.

Sit in a comfortable, relaxed posture. Draw your attention into the body.

Listen to the sounds around you.

Become aware of the sensations in your body.

Try to keep your eyes slightly open, gazing around one metre in front of you.

Then become completely mindful of your body, its shape and all the sensations you are experiencing.

These characteristics of your body are keeping your attention in the present moment.

When your mind wanders, use your awareness of the body to draw your attention to the moment.

Keeping the body still, merely be aware of it in a non-judgmental way.

Calmly abide, for as long as possible.

When you are ready to end the practice, dedicate your efforts, so you progress with your training and all the people in your life will benefit.

Through engaging with this practice and gradually developing insight, our concentration will become deeper, and we will gain a profound awareness of our body and its impermanent nature. During the day, we can use our awareness of the body to guide us into a peaceful, mindful state.

Rather than our body causing us to become self-conscious and agitated, always needing to be tended to and served, it can become a gentle anchor, helping us to connect with the present moment.

MINDFUL BREATHING

*Pacify stress with a series of essential
breathing meditations*

There are many mindful meditations that we can practise based on the breath. Mindful breathing meditations are practised across the world each day by millions of people. These practices are very accessible as we do not need any particular belief to get started and make progress. All we are doing is noting the natural process that sustains our life: the breath. In our culture, we are aware of the power of our breathing to pacify the mind. We say: 'Take a breather.' 'I need some breathing space.' 'Count ten breaths.' Emergency services are instructed to draw the attention of those whom they help to the sensation of their breath.

Already in this book, we have indirectly engaged in breathing practices. Listening to the breath, mindful listening, and mindful hands practice, all incorporate the breath. In this training, we are not directly drawing our attention to the breathing; we are easing our way into the flow of the breath. In mindful listening, we are merely attentive to the sounds around us and then inside us. The breath may be one of them.

When we place our hands on the stomach in the mindful hands practice, we are observing their rising and falling in time with the breath. We are not directly watching the breath; however, we will indirectly experience all the benefits of breathing meditation.

The reason I introduce the practices in this manner is that, when we first approach breathing meditation, our ego can be too intimately involved. When we are first instructed to bring our attention to the breath, it is natural to try and control it immediately. We almost try to make our breath happen.

Many times, when I introduce mindful breathing practices in live classes, new practitioners tend to exaggerate their breathing. We do not need to make ourselves breathe. It happens naturally. When we wake in the morning there is no need to jumpstart its process, it is just there, rising and falling naturally.

When we start to focus on mindful breathing, we try to follow its natural flow, a skill that we can cultivate and enjoy. It will then allow us to step back from the ego-driven mind that pushes, controls, and feels that we need to force things to happen if we want them to arise in our life. The breath occurs naturally, all we need to do is focus on it.

We know that there is a relationship between our mind and the breath, they are closely connected. Next time you are angry or see someone about to get angry, what happens to the breath? In the Northern hemisphere, we tend to hold our breath as a way to try to control our anger. When our breathing becomes rapid and shallow, it is usually because our mind is tight, nervous, and busy. As our mind starts to wind down, so does our breathing, it naturally slows and becomes deeper.

In some traditions and schools of meditation, there can be an encouragement to control the breath, to try and breathe deeply from the outset. Mindful breathing training is slightly different. Our breath becomes deeper as we start to focus on its natural flow. We do not need to alter it consciously.

To help encourage this, the first mindful breathing meditation that we engage in is the natural breath – the most simple and powerful practice. Even highly advanced meditators and yogis train in this practice, before entering more profound training. It is a great leveller and pacifier of the mind, a skill that will bring immediate benefit to our life.

Just as I am making notes for this book on the tram, the inspector's machine broke down and stopped issuing tickets. After a few attempts, his frustration was rising. What was the first thing he did? He took a deep breath in. We subconsciously know that our breath and mind are related. Mindful breathing helps us to establish what we already know: unite the body and mind, and you will bring peace into your life. When I used to teach Buddhist meditation, we ran a publicity campaign for a series of meditation classes, entitled, 'Peace is Closer Than You Think'. It is true; peace is right beneath our nose.

...

Natural Breath

A practice engaged in by millions
across the world each day

Sit in a relaxed, comfortable posture.
Bring your attention into the moment.

Listen mindfully to the sounds around you.
Gradually draw your attention inwards.

Slowly start to notice the natural rising and falling of your breath.

Follow the journey of your breath around the body.
As it enters, descends into your body, ascends and leaves.

Become one with the natural flow of the breath.

When your mind wanders, gradually bring it to the breath.
Bring your mind home to the breath as many times as possible.

Calmly abide and follow your breathing.
Stay with the process for as long as possible.

When you decide to finish your session, make the determination
to be mindful of your breathing throughout the day.

Dedicate the wholesome energy from your training so that your
mindful practice can benefit many people.

...

Daily Breath
A natural way to centre and refocus

Although it is essential to establish the habit of a quiet mindful practice each day and gradually increase the time we train, in general, in today's busy world we do not have an extensive amount of time to sit in meditation. With a creative approach, we can find many times during the day to practice. By turning our attention to the breath for a few moments, we establish a natural way to centre and refocus ourselves.

We can use the sound of our phone as a reminder to note the breathing. We transform our phone into a mindful bell. Our phone, instead of being a distraction, can encourage us to become present. Our phones may notify us many times during the day. If we are mindful this does not necessarily need to distract us; it all depends on how we relate to the update.

The endless e-notifications and subsequent reactions can bring a stream of nervousness into our body and mind that flows without interruption. Some people state that we should distance ourselves from technology feeling that it is inherently distracting. However, whether something is an object of distraction or not, depends solely upon our attitude of mind.

Our phones can distract us, but if we learn this breathing practice, they can help us to be more mindful, focused and concentrated. When our phone buzzes, instead of immediately answering, we use the sound and notification as a reminder to be mindful; take several breaths, and then check the phone.

There are many times we can use this breathing practice to bring a mindful focus to our day.

During the day, whether we like it or not, we must wait: while we are standing in a queue, at the traffic lights, in the doctor's or dentist's waiting room, waiting for the internet to load, or Wi-Fi to connect. Instead of filling this time with nervous energy, we use it to bring mindfulness into our lives. Mindful-while-we-wait practices are incredibly useful in creating a bridge between our formal meditation and daily life.

Think of all the times that life makes us wait. If we are creative, we can fill this waiting time with more than just a build up of nervous energy. We can transform these moments and discover that we do have time to practise and be mindful.

Many modern appliances function so they speed up some process or other, meaning we do not have to wait as long. They do not necessarily make our life more comfortable, as we end up filling the time that we would have waited with potentially nervous mental and physical activity.

Remembering to breathe mindfully we can give our mind a well-deserved rest, right in the middle of our busy day.

❖

As you are reading this, pause, and take a mindful breath.

...

We can take a few natural mindful breaths:

Before writing an email.

Upon receipt of a text.

When we are about to make an important decision.

When we are challenged or face some criticism.

When we feel ourselves retaliating.

When we wake in the morning.

Just before we sleep.

Before our morning coffee.

When we are about to set off for work.

When we pull up at a traffic light.

When we wait to cross the road.

When we wait in a queue.

Consider during your day when you could pause and mindfully breathe. Make the intention to put this breathing training into practice in your life; consequently, you will then enjoy all the peaceful benefits.

When we mindfully connect to our breath, we are celebrating being alive. Although a simple action, profound results will arise.

The solution to many of our problems, as stated by Henry David Thoreau in his seminal text, Walden, is to:

'Simplify, simplify, simplify'.

...

Subtle Breath

Discover a calm space, beneath the stress

This practice helps us to let go of our stress on a slightly deeper level. It is the next step from the natural breathing training and allows our mind to become subtler, naturally creating the cause for greater peace within. It is important to appreciate that it takes time to gather our mind inwards and away from distraction, especially if we are busy.

As we settle into the training, we will be able to enjoy a more subtle level of awareness; a more profound state of mind, not quite sleep, beneath and beyond stress. In the beginning, sleep can be an obstacle to our meditation, when our mind starts to become subtle, it is easy to drift off. If we are attentive with our practice, we can observe mental sinking occurring and prevent it by renewing our mindfulness and alertness. We enter a subtler level of consciousness.

We are taking an inner voyage. Our destination is inner peace and, along the route, we can visit deeper levels of calm and mental enjoyment. The subtle breath meditation helps us progress along this journey, moving away from our usual, everyday distractions.

...

Sit in a relaxed, upright posture for your practice.

Become mindfully aware of the sounds around you.

Draw your attention into the body. Notice the sensations.

Start to follow the natural flow of your breathing.

If you need assistance, place your hands on the stomach and observe the rising and falling of the breath.

Allow your mind to settle with the breathing. Follow the natural process.

Then start to draw your attention to the subtle sensation of the breath at the level of the nostrils.

Channel your concentration and focus on this area.

Notice the cool sensation as you breathe in, and the warm feeling as you breathe out.

Discover and try to locate where the sensation is, around the tip of the nostrils.

Place your careful attention on this sensation and allow a focus to develop.

If your mind wanders, bring it to back to the breathing and gradually draw your attention inwards, then start to focus on the subtle sensation.

This sensation of the breath is your object of meditation, if your mind becomes distracted, bring your attention to its flow.

Practise like this for as long as you can.

Before finishing, dedicate all the good energy from your training so you can continue with your practice, and it will benefit all the people in your life.

...

When we train like this, before we sit down to practice, it is good to have a definite object of meditation; encouraging a greater focus and development of the mind. If we can establish a professional approach to our meditation, we will grow into the practice and see internal progress. In the breathing training introduced above, the object of our meditation is our subtle breath. We bring our attention to this object, whenever our mind wanders. No matter how distracted our mind may be, we keep returning it to the object of meditation. Patiently and steadily, we train our mind.

In the Buddhist meditation texts, they talk about binding the rope of our mind to the stake of mindfulness. In a relaxed, consistent manner, we are determined and dedicated to remain with our object of meditation.

...

Tune into the Breath

Finding balance during the day

It is often the case that what we are looking for is located right under our nose. Although the sensation of the breath is occurring continuously, we may have not yet connected to it with single-pointed concentration. Try to tune into the breathing during the day, whenever possible, and enjoy a subtler level of mind, beyond the stress. Notice that subtle sensation at the tip of the nostrils.

As our mind pacifies through focusing on the breathing it is naturally less frustrated and anxious, thus becoming more peaceful. The more habituated we become to training in a quiet environment, the more we will be able to meet our breath at busier moments during the day, thereby both capable and confident to maintain a mindful awareness continually.

...

Counting the Breath

Improving our concentration and focus

Counting our breathing can help strengthen our focus and concentration, as we have a hook to help our mind stay present.

When I visit schools to introduce mindful meditation, I notice that this practice works well with children. It is as though we are playing a little mindful game by keeping our busy mind occupied with counting. It also works well with teaching staff. In fact, it is one of the most helpful mindful practices for people of all ages. We have something familiar to focus on, and we can monitor the progress of our concentration. We count the breathing to retain a focus and keep our attention stabilised.

The breath is subtle and almost intangible. In the beginning, counting the breath helps to stabilise our practice and provides us with a sense of how we are progressing with our training. We combine focusing on the natural breath with counting each out-breath. When our mind becomes distracted, start counting from zero again.

Try to count three exhalations initially and then progress to ten, gradually and gently increase your capacity to focus. Our single-pointed concentration will become stronger as we train in this method.

...

Gather your attention into the present moment. Listen to the sounds around you.

Become aware of the sensations within your body.

Start to focus on the sensation of your breathing, observe the natural flow. Stay with this for a short time.

Each time you breathe out, mentally count the exhalation.

Breathe in. Breathe out, count one. Calmly abide, emphasising your focus on the out-breath; count in a relaxed manner. See if you can count five rounds of out-breath.

One. Two. Three. Four. Five. Counting five complete rounds of breath without distraction is a great start.

When your mind becomes distracted, come back to the first round of breath and start counting again.

Keep this process going until your mind becomes distracted, then return to the first round of breathing.

If you can count five rounds of breath, then challenge yourself to see if you can gradually progress to ten rounds.

Keep counting in a relaxed way. When your mind is distracted from the breath return it immediately.

Engage with the practice for as long as possible; keep coming to the breath and the process of counting.

Just before you finish, dedicate the mindful energy so that you can continue with your practice and it will benefit many people.

...

In one of the live classes that I teach, one participant said that she could only count one breath and kept becoming distracted after this first round. She was initially quite disheartened. I said, 'when we train in meditation, it is a gradual process, the most important element of the training is our ability to bring our attention to the object of meditation – our breath.' I said to the lady, 'at least you managed one breath!' We allow positive thinking to influence us. If we can only count one round of breath in the beginning, then this is our starting point. If we can accept this as a foundation, we will slowly make progress.

...

Zen Breath

Following the journey of our breath around the body

The Japanese word 'Zen' in English means 'meditation'. This ancient tradition of practice has greatly influenced the modern mindfulness movement. Zen is a school of meditation that has mindful practices right at its heart, and here we are going to draw influence from this training. One of the essential components of Zen practice is simplicity, minimising the analysis. Not adding anything that is not already there, taking a less is more approach.

In this Zen breath training, we sit and observe; following the full flow and cycle of our breathing. The practice itself will lead naturally to the present moment and allow us to have an objective approach to our thoughts. The breath itself is not a narrow phenomenon; it is a broad flowing, dynamic experience. Zen breathing helps us to connect and thoroughly enjoy this process. Let us now take a look at how we can practise Zen breathing.

...

❖

Bring your attention to the present moment. Notice the sensations of your body. Bring your awareness within.

Draw your attention to the full sensation of the breath.

Focus on the full flow of breathing entering and leaving your body.

Try to follow the complete journey of your breath, as it travels around the body.

Notice the sensation entering your body, its descent into your lungs and ascent as it leaves.

Try not to strain as you watch the breathing; apply just enough effort to keep your mind focused and relaxed.

Observe the cycle of breath. Try to become one with the process.

You are practising Zen breathing.

Stay with this process for as long as possible.

As the practice concludes, dedicate all the good energy from your training, so that it will benefit many people in your life.

...

Allowing the Mind to Settle

Just this

Try not to overthink your meditation, by assessing yourself, continuously monitoring each development, or focusing on what seems to be a lack of progress. Just try to follow the flow and cycle of daily practice; our training will start to answer the questions we have. When we have a question about meditation, we can often find the answer we are looking for within the question.

When the mind starts to settle, and we can be patient enough, we will find answers to many of our questions, in the space of our quiet, meditation practice.

...

Compassionate Breath

Encouraging our good heart to grow

In the mindful heart chapter, we will explore in more detail the practice of compassion. Here is an introduction to how we can combine compassion with our breathing, thereby enriching our meditation practice. Compassion is when we have the wish for all living beings to be free from their suffering, problems and difficulties. Based on a reflection of what life would be like in someone else's shoes, we open our heart to the lives of others. We reflect: due to being born human, whatever our status, we have to undergo underlying anxiety. Just like us, everyone has to endure uncertainty, worry and confusion. We feel in our heart:

'Wouldn't it be wonderful if all living beings could be free from their problems and difficulties.'

This contemplation encourages a good heart to arise for those in our life and society, which we can use in this mindful breathing practice. It is a simple, powerful, and beautiful meditation.

...

Sit in a relaxed, comfortable posture for meditation. Bring your attention to the present moment.

Notice the sensations in your body. Start to observe your breathing and follow your natural breath.

Allow your mind to settle gradually.

Imagine yourself surrounded by friends, family and loved ones.

If you want to develop great compassion, try to visualise as many people as possible in the circle around you.

Over time, with practice, practitioners can expand and develop their compassionate circle.

Start to notice the in-breath.

With each inhalation cultivate the wish for yourself to be free from problems and difficulties.

Spend a little time just noticing the in-breath and engaging with this reflection.

Start to abide with the out-breath. Calmly develop the wish for those around you to be free from suffering.

Combine compassion with your breathing. Try to focus on your compassionate breath for as long as possible.

Try to feel compassion in your heart, as opposed to thinking about it. Follow this process for as long as you can.

Calmly abide.

Towards the end of your session, imagine that your wish has come about; that you and others have become free from suffering. Try to hold this belief for the remainder of your session.

Just before you finish, dedicate your training so it will benefit many people and so that we will all be able to find freedom from the problems and difficulties in our lives.

❖

...

The breathing element of this practice helps us to stay focused and in the present moment; adding compassion encourages the good heart to grow and develop within us. The meditations in the mindful heart chapter will explain the practice of compassion in more detail. It is enough at this point, to combine our compassionate mind with our breath.

...

Mindful breathing sits at the heart of our meditation practice. Try to establish a foundation, by continually engaging in the training presented here. All these breathing practices help to pacify worry, so are particularly suitable for these busy, modern times.

If we are interested in reducing the stress and anxiety in our mind and the lives of others it is essential to engage in these mindfulness practices. We can also share them with our friends and family when they are feeling nervous, tense and fearful.

Depending on our circumstances, the amount of time we engage with mindful breathing can range from a few seconds up to many hours each day, if we are at a meditation retreat. There is no right time in our life or a particular type of person that we must be, or diet that we must follow, to commence this beneficial habit. We just sit and begin, then slowly we will start to make progress.

Millions of people across the world are practising mindful breathing. From busy office workers, spending a few seconds each day in their chairs at work, bringing their attention to the breath when they are experiencing stress. All the way through to monks in remote Buddhist temples in Thailand sitting for up to ten hours a day in the lotus posture, edging towards nirvana. Whatever our capacity, if we sit and start to breathe mindfully we will begin to enjoy all the extraordinary benefits.

...

There are many mindful breathing practices. I have presented some essential meditations in this chapter. For daily practice, I recommend Zen Breathing.

MINDFUL MIND

*Developing emotional intelligence
and stillness*

One of the aspects of our training that can be elusive for us is the actualisation of peace, clarity, and relaxation. Although we may associate these experiences with mindful meditation practice, they may not have arisen in our consciousness. Depending on our approach, the effects of mindful practice can seem distant and hard work to obtain.

Sometimes, when practitioners first start to meditate they have a continuous flow of distractions. It seems as though they have more thoughts than before. This process is known as the 'waterfall effect'. When we train in mindful sitting practices it can seem like a mini-battle is taking place between us, the person who is meditating, and our distractions – with distractions often seemingly coming out victorious. One comment that arises, again and again, amongst new meditators who attend my classes, is: 'I find it hard to clear my mind. I cannot seem to clear my head of distractions.'

This conclusion can arise because we try to impose peace and calm upon our mind. We have an image of what a clear mind should be like, and we hastily try to fabricate this within. This approach does not help us to abide in the present moment and can cause more stress and activity to arise in our mind.

The next series of practices can help us to avoid this way of approaching our training and empower us to learn how to enjoy our mind, and recognise the peace that resides beyond our distractions. We can learn how to stop battling, forcing and struggling with our thoughts in meditation, and instead, start to enjoy an experience of deep relaxation.

...

Just Sitting

Allowing our mind to settle and thoughts to harmonise

Sit in a relaxed, comfortable, and alert meditation posture.

Bring your attention to the present moment.

Become aware of all the sensations within your body.

Gradually notice the sensation of your breathing.

Try to follow the natural breath as it arises and dissolves.

Allow your mind to settle as it connects with the breathing.

When your mind focuses, observe yourself sitting. Turn your attention to the mind and notice your thoughts as they pass.

Try not to follow and entertain the activity that is arising within your mind. Simply watch your thoughts as they arise and dissolve.

Practise as though you were sitting on the side of a river, just watching the flow of the water, observe and notice everything in the river floating by, but try not to become entangled.

Sit for a short time and do nothing other than watch your mind.

When your attention becomes distracted by thoughts that take you away from the present moment, bring yourself inward, observe your mind and watch again.

Just sit, looking calmly at your mind, with non-judgmental awareness.

Mindful of your mind and the thoughts that pass.

Quietly, observing the mind.
Keep gently bringing your attention to the present moment.

Engage with this practice for as long as possible.
Just sitting and accepting whatever is arising in your mind.

Just before your meditation ends, dedicate all the positive energy from your practice so you can progress with your training and it will benefit many people.

...

With this practice, we are starting to explore 'not doing'. Instead of something, nothing. Don't just do something, sit there. In our busy, 'doing world', to 'not do' can seem like an alien concept. Everything is designed around doing something. Observe our conversations: 'What shall we do this weekend?' 'What shall we do now?' 'What shall we do tonight?' 'Let's do something today!'

It can seem that if we are busy and do many things, we are leading a meaningful life. Even to solve our problems, when we are going through difficulties, we are advised to be busy. 'Just keep busy, and you'll get through it.' When we learn to meditate, if we are not mindful of our approach and intention, it can become something that we must do; our mindful meditation practice goes on our to-do busy list.

The thought of meditation can even stress us out: 'Oh no, I haven't done my meditation!' Then when we try to meditate, it can seem like a great effort. The process feels difficult. Our busy mind keeps assessing our problems and making judgments about our progress, creating stress and tension within our mind.

The just sitting practice helps to counteract this. As a result of allowing the mind to settle and our thoughts to harmonise, we can start to relax.

We can become so completely present that the mind becomes clear and crystal. We may have experienced this when we have been away on holiday, enjoying nature, or perhaps immersed in creation, maybe painting, writing, or composing music. It can feel like time slows down, as though it is almost stopping, and we become one with the moment. We cannot fabricate this or look for it, as it is already here.

We have many different levels of mind ranging from gross to very subtle. In our daily life, we mainly have grosser levels of distracted minds. When we first start to meditate, we are mentally crowded within our busy conceptions; it can be challenging to manage, pacify and control them. It can feel as though we are locked in a dark room with our thoughts. When we can learn to sit and let our mind naturally settle into the present moment, it will become subtler and more peaceful.

If we reflect on the water in a lake, if there is movement, the clarity is clouded when the sediment from the floor is agitated. When there is less movement, and the lake calms, the sediment settles, and the water becomes clear. The same occurs with our mind; when it relaxes and is allowed to settle down, its peaceful nature arises. With the just sitting practice, we are not going anywhere; we calmly abide in the present moment. Being nobody, going nowhere.

What a relief that we can finally stop. How relaxing this practice can be for us. From time-to-time, instead of doing something, try not doing and see what happens. It is almost as though this practice goes beyond mindful meditation.

...

Silent Watcher

Abide within the moment

The essence of mindful practice is to abide in the present with non-judgmental awareness. In the silent watcher training, we sit, observing our body and mind, noticing whatever is happening around and inside of us. We become the 'silent watcher', observing but not commentating. The key to this practice is to watch with a non-judgmental awareness in an open, accommodating manner.

...

Sit in a relaxed but alert posture to practise. Make the intention that you are training not just for yourself, but on behalf of others.

Watch what is taking place inside your mind.
Note your thoughts. Let them arise and dissolve.

Observe what is happening inside your body.
Watch your thoughts, try to almost see through them.

Without following or assessing, merely observe.

Try to remain physically still, but not rigid, gradually turning your mind inwards.

It is like you are in a forest, watching what is taking place: the movement of the trees, the sound of nature, even animals moving in and out of view.

You sit perfectly quiet and watch. All you can hear is the sound of your breath.

If you were to sit in an unknown, tropical forest, interested to see the different animals that had made it their home but were not sure which beasts you were going to see, and what their size may be. You would stay completely still and attentive. You would be the silent watcher. Just in case. It is the same here. You are not entirely sure what thoughts are going to come, but when they do, you have the presence of mind to let them pass.

You watch; sitting and silently noticing.

Calmly abide in the present moment.

Sit for as long as possible.

As your practice concludes, dedicate all the good wholesome energy from your training, so that it benefits many people in your life.

When you have finished the practice, make time during the day to watch the world go by, try not to believe judgments and projections, observe, and give yourself the mental freedom to let your thoughts pass.

We have five senses through which we filter our world. Our mind is like our sixth sense; it can watch and observe. Mindful meditation is an experience of mind.

...

Cloud Watching

Let the clouds of distraction pass
through the clear blue sky

When we meditate on the mind, we are taking our practice to a subtler level. To be able to focus depends on having cultivated our concentration during the previous mindful practices.

When we talk about the mind, we cannot point to a picture of it, or say that it smells like this, or looks like that, because it is abstract and non-physical, and cannot be experienced by our senses

It is for this reason that we are going to introduce analogies to our contemplations. Analogies can help point us in the right direction in our meditations; once we start to get a feeling of the meaning of the analogy, we can let it go. They are a means to an end and not designed to distract us from the present moment.

For example, in this cloud watching practice. By thinking too much about what types of clouds we are observing, what their shape and colour is, and where in the world we are, we will bring too much conceptual detail to our training, and take our self away from the scent of the meditation, which is to bring us into the present moment.

With the cloud watching practice, we reflect on a very well-known analogy that goes back to the time of Buddha. Our thoughts and conceptions are like clouds arising and dissolving out of the sky of our mind. If we observe the sky, watching clouds pass, we will see how they manifest, take shape, abide and then gradually dissolve. The same process of arising and dissolving occurs with our thoughts if we mindfully watch them. We do not follow our thoughts; we let them pass.

So we use the analogy, but do not need to turn our thoughts into clouds. We do not need to visualise our thoughts inside the clouds. The simple analogy is enough, using the imagery as a way to gain an insight into the practice. We are open to thoughts, curious to see, and gentle in our treatment of them.

As the great Zen master Shunryu Suzuki, instructed, we invite our thoughts, but we do not serve them tea.

...

❖

Sit in a relaxed, comfortable position and bring your attention gently to the present moment, moving away from thoughts about the future and the past.

Become aware of the sounds, and the environment around you. Use the sensation of your breath, to help you focus the mind.

If you need assistance with concentrating, try counting ten rounds of breath. Then step back from the breath, sit and draw your attention inwards.

Observe your mind.

Imagine your thoughts are like clouds arising out of the sky of your subtle mind. Look at the sky of your mind itself, and try not to become engrossed by thoughts. Let them pass.

When you find yourself becoming entangled with concepts, try not to follow or be misled by them, come back to the present moment and allow your attention to absorb inwards to the deeper level of mind.

Keep up this visualisation, when your mind begins to absorb and focus, then let go of the imagery, sit and watch.

If your mind is overflowing with distractions and it is difficult to find any clarity, then return to the process of counting the breath and allow your mind to concentrate.

Once your mind concentrates through focusing on the breath, return to the practice of watching the thoughts.

Engage with the training for as long as possible.

When you are ready to conclude the practice, dedicate all the good energy you have created so it can benefit many people, and you can progress with your training.

In your daily life, as often as you can, look up at the sky. Reflect on the clouds, how they arise and disappear. Allow any stressful, busy minds to dissolve into the immensity of the sky. Just watch your world pass. Take a step back from the digital treadmill of modern life and tune into the present moment.

...

Ocean Waves

Using an ancient visualisation to take our practice deeper

We continue with watching our mind, using analogies to help with the process. This contemplation dates back thousands of years to the ancient Buddhist philosophical scriptures from India. We reflect that our root or subtle mind is like a vast ocean and our thoughts are like waves, arising from this ocean. We can use this analogy in meditation to take us deeper into our mind and the present moment.

Sit in a relaxed, comfortable meditation posture and draw your attention inwards. Listen to the sounds around you. These are the sounds of the present moment.

Become aware of the sensations within your body.

Focus on the sensation of your breathing.

Become attentive to your thoughts, as they pass through your mind.

While gathering your attention inwards, reflect on the analogy of how your mind is like an ocean. As your thoughts arise, reflect on how they are merely waves emerging from the ocean of your mind. Watch these waves of thoughts as they arise and dissolve.

It is as though you were sitting on the beach watching the ocean. Patiently observe the process.

Allow the waves of distraction to settle into your vast ocean mind.

When you feel present, slowly let go of the analogy and watch the mind itself.

Just sit for as long as possible, looking at the mind. Calmly abide in the present moment. When you are ready to conclude your session, dedicate your practice, so it benefits many people, and you can continue to progress with your training.

Intend to hold the analogy of the ocean and waves in your daily life. Try to improve your understanding of the nature of the relationship between your mind and the world that appears to it.

...

In daily life, we can reflect on how what appears to our mind is a reflection. The appearances in our life are like waves arising from the ocean of our mind. Notice how when the mind is peaceful and calm, the world that appears to it seems more agreeable. On the other hand, when our mind is anxious, tense and uptight, then the world around us appears less pleasing.

If we can appreciate this, then we can understand how the quality of our mind influences the world that appears to it. We can take a more objective approach, which empowers us with the ability to let go, relax, and have confidence in the mind's ability to affect authentic change.

The more insight we have in the power that our mind has to influence and improve our lives, the more energy we will put into our mindful meditation practice.

...

Zen Mind

Incorporating all the practices
we have learned thus far

The modern presentation of mindfulness is hugely indebted to the Zen teachings. In this ancient tradition of meditation, we are mainly encouraged to sit and meditate. To go directly to the present moment, bypassing intellectual analysis. We can read many teachings on the subject of Zen and attend classes, workshops and retreats, but there is no replacement for actual practice. The training is not academic.

In modern education, we are trained to think rationally and critically. It is natural, therefore, that when we first learn mindful practices, we approach them analytically, and can miss having an authentic encounter with our practice. Our intellect can erect a barrier between our head and the heart of awareness.

Interestingly, within ancient Zen monasteries, being allocated menial tasks was seen as a promotion, providing those who were assigned them the opportunity to engage in mindful movement. Work that required physical movement was sought-after, as it allowed the practitioner to seamlessly abide in the present moment and connect smoothly with the ground of their practice.

The appearance of Zen Buddhism in the USA in the late 1950s coincided with the foundation of Nike. The philosophy influenced its founders. Nike's slogan 'Just Do It' has undertones of Zen.

In this training, we are engaged in direct practice. We try to abide in the present moment, not rushing forward, or stuck in the past. The stress, worry and anxiety in our life arises from being caught up in one of these two extremes. In this section, I will introduce a mindful training that incorporates all the mindful practices we have learned thus far, leading us to one, complete, essential meditation.

When we train in the mindful mind it helps to have as our foundation, a progressive experience of the mindful listening, mindful body and mindful breathing practices, revealed in the previous three chapters. On retreats, I gradually introduce this series of practices, over the first three sessions, leading organically to the mindful mind.

All the four practices combined are like a set of Russian dolls. You have the main one – the mindful mind – which also contains within it the previous three mindful meditations. The large doll contains other dolls although you cannot initially see them.

We will now learn one essential mindful meditation that has inside it all the other rich meditative practices we have learned thus far. I like to call this training, 'Zen Mind'.

We are entering into a deeper space of meditation. As we go into each practice, we let go of the previous one. If our mind becomes distracted, we can return to the earlier training. As we meet our distractions, we relax, gently drawing our attention naturally into the body, then gradually gathering our attention to the breathing, and then the mind. Becoming distracted is natural. The degree to which we become distracted will then direct us to which mindful practice to use, to help draw our attention into the present moment.

...

If distractions take you outside the room, use mindful listening to hook your attention to the body, breath and mind. If it is just a little distraction but your attention is still in the room, come to your body, then breath, then mind. This returning process can be done in ten-to-twenty second periods until your mind is settled again in the present. Zen mind is a practice that can provide you with a daily basis for your mindful training.

1. Read slowly, initially, and then gradually start to memorise.

2. Sit in a relaxed but attentive posture to practise meditation.

3. Become aware of the sounds around you, mindfully listen, with an open, non-judgmental awareness.

4. Start to notice the sensations of your body.

5. Focus on the natural flow of the breath.

6. Allow your mind to settle.

7. Sit and watch the mind, calmly abide, observe each moment.

If your mind wanders, then depending on the degree of distraction go through steps two to six again, until your attention draws back. Repeat steps six and seven for as long as possible.

  As you bring your practice to a completion, dedicate all the mindful energy so that you can continue with your training.

...

The Zen mind practice that we are training in here is the accumulation of the first four chapters and provides a complete, mindful meditation practice. The next four chapters will guide, explain and encourage us to carry mindful awareness gently and smoothly into our daily actions. If we can integrate our practice, we will be able to bring our training to life and cause it to be of benefit to all the people in our society. We will naturally be able to single task, slow down, and shine the light of our attention on each moment of our existence.

MINDFUL MOVEMENT

Establishing a dynamic mindfulness practice

In the next two chapters, we consider our activities when we are not meditating, which, for the majority of people, is most of the time. We will explore in more depth some of the practices briefly mentioned in previous chapters, reflecting on how we can carry our mindful training into daily life.

We are constantly moving. Even when we sit still our mind is moving forward and backwards, side to side, up and down; there is no stopping it. This almost continuous unsettled mind means we find it challenging to settle both physically and mentally. How can we transform this busy movement into mindful activity? To begin with, it can help to slow down our actions so that we can gain an insight into the mindful way. We do not necessarily need to engage in all our activities slowly; however, it can be helpful in the early stages of our training.

Our mind can be so busy thinking and worrying about what we are going to do next that we miss what we are doing, right now. The precious moments of our life can pass us by, as a result of being two or three moments ahead of, or behind, ourselves. When we start to slow down our movement, it is easier to engage in what we are doing mindfully.

We can start with our walking. In many respects, walking is similar to breathing. It is something that we do all the time, yet we are rarely fully aware of the process. When we took our first steps, it was incredible; we were able to immerse in the present moment. Now due to familiarity and busyness, the steps we take can be mechanical, merely taking us to the next job we must do, the next task in our life. With this approach, our body can become just like a machine.

With mindful awareness, our body becomes a vessel for encouraging the growth of mindfulness, and each step we take leads us closer to inner peace. When we walk mindfully, we can watch, observe, breathe, and fully take in the changing world around us.

As mentioned the translation of the word Buddha in Sanskrit is 'Awakened One'. Awakened from what exactly? He has awoken from the sleep of confusion. The confusion of the distracted, conceptual mind that deprives us of a full experience of human life. The distracted mind seeks novelty, change, busyness, speed, making everything seem like a race, thus pushing us away from the present moment.

To feel present, we may feel the need to engage in extreme activities. For example, extreme sports force us to have a complete focus and concentration on the moment, or we lose everything. As our lives tend to be relatively safe and taken up with routine, the ability we have to be completely present rarely needs exercising. Maybe we have glimpses of being fully present when we connect with someone and experience flashes of joy, or when we immerse in the beauty of nature, drawn in by some transcending music or work of art; these moments pass, and we can be left seeking out the next experience that will help us to feel fully alive. We can also look for deep and profound insights in our meditation practice to try and grasp the moment, which can function to draw us away from the present.

We can search outside ourselves, travel to far off places, explore book after book, gather and collect experiences to try and have a precious, meaningful life. We can feel the need to drive towards the extraordinary. It can seem the mundane is not worthy of our full attention, and that we need to distract ourselves from it, moving towards the new and unusual.

We walk to travel, to move, sometimes we are forced to march by our busy mind, to tread on the earth with force, stress and impatience. To strive towards the next accomplishment, and then the next, continually. One of my Buddhist teachers shared an analogy that I found humorous and poignant regarding this; he said it is like we are on a conveyor belt, rushing in one direction and at some point, the conveyor belt ends, and we drop off!

The natural habit of a busy mind is that even when we are on the conveyor belt, it is distracted from what is happening right now. Our mind can be continually ahead of where we are, even if it is just three or four moments. A student who comes to my live classes was laughing, telling me about his busy mind; smiling, he said that he is always ahead of himself, even when going to the toilet, he quickly flushes before completion!

Confucius famously stated: *'Wherever we go, there we are.'* Mindful movement can help us to gain insight into these profound words.

If we were to travel to Copenhagen, upon arrival, we would say, 'I am in Copenhagen'. As soon as we have this thought, we can miss the present moment. We may read a guidebook, gather opinions, take photographs, walk around looking and gazing at the city, but completely miss Copenhagen. During our stay, we can rely on our conceptual idea of what Copenhagen is, instead of experiencing the city directly.

As Plato described in his analogy of the cave, we do not see Copenhagen; we filter it through our intellectual understanding. If we are in Copenhagen and genuinely mindful, acknowledging what is happening moment by moment, it does not even require us to think, 'I am in Copenhagen'.

How can we understand this concerning our practice of mindful walking? If we were to walk around Copenhagen mindfully, we would be aware of the process of walking, noticing the sensation of the ground, listening to the sounds around us, the feelings in our body, and walk around entirely in the present moment. Occasionally, those who have taken hallucinogenic drugs gain insight into this awareness, but it's very fleeting, and the mind runs ahead of itself, away from the present moment.

If we train in mindful walking, then our moment-by-moment focus is heightened. We notice everything that is happening around and inside of us, yet distracted by nothing. As George Harrison sang: *'Life goes on, within you and without you.'* Through increasing our mindful awareness, we can start to appreciate the meaning of these words and have a harmonious engagement with our life.

Some meditation traditions talk about energy or chi; in Star Wars they refer to a force that the Jedi connects with, and some faiths refer to Brahma, God, Indra, and Buddha. In this book, we will not use these words or concepts. We are just learning to watch and experience what is happening in each moment.

We start to go beyond the ordinary, distracted mind and begin to tap into the present moment to gain a deeper, clearer connection with what is arising. As our mind wanders into our head, and then into distraction away from the moment, we gently draw our attention to the body. The sensations that pass through our body are reminding us of where we are.

Instead of our body distracting us and being a cause for confusion and a basis for our difficulties, we transform it into a powerful reminder of the present. In reality, we do not come back to the present. We go into the moment using our breath to draw us in and away from the distractions that rob us of having a satisfying and contented life.

As we walk mindfully in our world, with each step, we can potentially turn a new page, and leave the past behind. A street that we have walked down thousands of times can appear new, when we see it through mindful, fresh eyes.

A practitioner from one of my classes recounted when she engaged in this training for the first time. She was noticing everything around her and conscious of each footstep. During her walk, she looked down and saw a five-pound note. She recounted that she would have easily walked past it if she had been in her usual, busy, autopilot mode. This little reward encouraged her to continue practising.

We are changing and working with our inner world, and as a result, our outer world transforms. Distractions, worry and anxiety blind our mindful eye and deprive us of having a rich experience of life.

With mindful walking, we come to transcend the mundane, distracted world as we descend into the present moment. The great Zen master, Shunryu Suzuki, explains that there is no real difference between our inner and outer worlds; our breath acts as a swinging door between the two. This practice, and the effects arising from it guide us into reality. For this practice, no change or alteration is necessary from the outside, all we need to do is lightly adjust our focus and perception.

When our busy mind is captain of the vessel of our existence, we are marched and rushed forward continually away from the moment. In this practice, it is the walker itself that we are concerned with, not the future destination. We bring our awareness to the actual striving and pushing. We go into the waves of distraction and discover the vast ocean beneath. If we can focus on walking, and nothing else, then we naturally relax into the moment and can move mindfully through our world. Let us now explore how we can practise this in our daily life.

...

Mindful Walking: Formal

Combining our walking with the breathing

Initially, I recommend engaging with this training indoors, where there are fewer distractions. After you have gained some experience, take your practice outdoors. When I guide one-day retreats, I take practitioners into a forest, and we train in mindful walking within a clearing in the wood. We will look at this outdoor practice in more detail in a few pages. When you first start to train in mindful walking, give yourself around ten minutes and go very slowly.

You can walk from one side of your room to the other, or walk in a circle around your room.

Start in the mindful standing posture, with your back straight, shoulders relaxed, feet pointed outwards, rooted and grounded on the floor.

Spend a few moments in this posture, drawing your attention into the present moment.

Then start to focus on the inhalation of your breath.

As you breathe in, raise your right foot, an average height, as though you were going to take a step.

As you breathe out, let your foot touch the floor, and take a small step, move forward.

As you breathe in again, raise your left foot and as you breathe out, place it on the floor, taking your next small step.

Continue like this, walking carefully, slowly, and mindfully.

As you progress, the process starts to become more natural.

Feel the sensation of your feet on the ground.

Try to have a good upright posture with your shoulders relaxed as you walk.

Place your hands by your sides or clasp them gently in front of you.

We combine the process of walking with our breathing.

We completely slow down the process of walking and mindfully capture each step.

Each time you breathe in, raise your foot; as you breathe out, place it on the ground.

Caress the floor with your feet. Tread on the earth with presence, peace, and kindness.

To begin with, you may need to look down slightly, to avoid becoming off balance. As you progress, look ahead, with an upright, noble posture.

Relax in the present moment and engage with the method for as long as you feel comfortable.

Notice all the different sensations arising in your body.

Let thoughts about the past and the future dissolve, without entertaining them.

When you are ready to bring your practice to a close, make the determination that you are going to walk mindfully through your life for the benefit of everyone in your society.

❖

...

Mindful Walking: Informal

Moving naturally into the moment

In the previous practice, we engaged in a formal mindful walking training by completely slowing down the process, combining each step with our breathing. I recommend starting a mindful walking practice indoors where there are fewer distractions and then taking the practice outside.

When we decide to progress and take our practice outside, there will potentially be more phenomena to distract our senses. With experience, we can learn to transform these distractions and use them to enhance our mindful training.

When we start outside, it is good to use a quiet location such as in our garden, in the early morning on the beach, in the forest or a quiet area in the local park. Appreciating that with all the mindful practices presented here, we try to train in such a way that we do not draw unnecessary attention to ourselves. The key to having a long-lasting practice is that we can integrate our training fully into our society, without appearing different or unusual in any way.

When we have more confidence in the practices, we can then take them into busier environments. Internally we are practising, but externally there is no need to show or demonstrate that this is the case.

Start walking at your normal pace, try to concentrate on the physical process and the sensations in your body. Try just to walk.

As you find the rhythm and thread of your practice, start to notice everything around you, without being distracted from the moment.

Notice your breath and allow it to bring you into the present moment.

Through engaging with this training, you can become relaxed and energised by your natural environment.

During your mindful walk, occasionally stop, stand mindfully and try to become aware of everything around you.

Breathe it all in, and as you exhale let all your distractions and stress dissolve away.

Practise for as long as you feel comfortable.

Before you finish your walk, dedicate the good energy so that it will bring peace into your life and the world around you.

...

Urban Walking
Peace in the city

Each day we must walk. Even if we have to spend a considerable amount of our time sitting and travelling by car, we still need to walk to the car from our house, walk to the bathroom from the bed, or walk around our workplace. Each time we walk, we can take the opportunity to tune into the present moment; recharge and unwind the mind.

When we practise this style of mindful walking, all we need to do is bring our attention to the natural process. There is no need to slow down our action. We notice our posture while becoming aware of the sensation of our feet on the ground. Slightly straightening the back brings our awareness to the present moment. Also, gently touching the fingers against the palms of the hands can help to draw us into the body.

Think of all the short walks that we take during the day; with skilful awareness, we can transform them into mindfulness practices. Mindful walking guides us into the present moment, without too much effort or fuss. We are firstly establishing a habit of mind, which then naturally will influence our physical actions.

Initially, we need to encourage ourselves to remember and engage, deciding to be mindful through the day. Over time, with familiarity, our practice becomes natural. Even though we are not making a show of our training, those around us may start to notice a gradual change in our behaviour,

For example, when we train in mindful movement, we may move around our world in a quieter manner. We may also remember where we put down our keys, and others personal items, so we stop losing things, thus saving our self valuable time, and meaning that we do not have to go through the unnecessary anxiety of trying to find lost items. We will naturally be more considerate when we walk in public, perhaps opening doors for people and letting them pass first; also mindful not to stand in the way of others, which can easily happen if we are mentally elsewhere.

In short, we become a more considerate citizen of the world, solely through being a little more attentive to the steps that we take on this planet. Living in this busy, distracted, striving, aspirational world, it is indeed a vital and necessary practice.

Through the familiarity we have gained in our previous mindful training, we will find ourselves naturally practising mindful walking more and more, without needing any encouragement.

With urban walking, we make the intention to step out for a walk in the city, not going anywhere special, just walking.

...

Determine, before you set out to train, to be attentive and awake as you walk. If you wish, you can set a time to practise.

Even as you put on your shoes, notice the entire process, the small steps. There is no rush. You are slowing right down.

Notice the sensation of your feet against your shoes and the floor.

Be in the moment as you open the door to go outside, as you touch the door, and as you lock the door.

You are not rushing forward, just being present, being here.

Step out, and just before you start walking, feel the atmosphere in the air. Feel the sensations against your skin. Listen to the different sounds around you.

The smells that arise and dissolve. Take a few mindful breaths. Then start walking at your natural pace.

If you are a quick walker, you may find yourself slowing down, as you are not on a mission to go anywhere.

You are going nowhere in particular.

Start to become aware of your entire body, the sensations and its contact with the earth. Breathe into the moment and allow your body to caress the floor as you walk.

Feel the bones in your feet and the muscles at work in your body, keeping you upright. Try not to worry or overthink; there is no right way to do this practice.

When you start to become familiar with the physical process, take in the cityscape around you. Watch it arise, appear and dissolve.

Images and snapshots of people's lives, coming and going, in and out of our vision.

Just like thoughts that were arising and dissolving in previous sitting meditations in the mindful mind chapter, the visual appearances appear and disappear similarly.

It is almost as if you are in a three hundred and sixty-degree cinedome of the mind. You are walking through the city, but are no longer trying to control anything, or even make anything happen.

You are just watching, observing, reflecting, and letting go.

As you walk around the city, start to notice the detail.

Distraction no longer guides you.
You allow yourself to go deeper into reality.

The ground you walk on: thousands of people worked exceptionally hard to keep it level, to make it smooth for you to travel comfortably. The materials used, potentially collected from all corners of the globe.

These thoughts are not distractions, just observations, arising like waves in the ocean.

Keep gradually bringing your attention into the present moment. Observe the mind as it wanders, then naturally bring yourself back.

Continue with your walk as long as you wish.

❖

...

We can practise mindfulness in many environments and locations. When we practise in the city, it may be challenging to begin with, as there are so many entangling distractions that take our attention away from the present moment. However, if we reflect: something becomes a distraction based on how we relate to it. The city and all it offers do not need to sway us away from the present moment if we can learn to immerse into the practice.

It may appear that to go deeper into our meditation practice, to let go of all the busyness, we need to retreat to the country and immerse with nature. Withdrawing can help the process, but it is helpful to appreciate, that with confidence we can practice wherever we are.

My journey is of living in a retreat located in the country for ten years during my twenties. This time was helpful in the beginning, to focus and gain a deep insight into meditation practice without being waylaid by the distractions of the city. In my thirties, I moved to live and teach in a more urban environment. In the city, I learned the busyness could lead to inner peace and calm; it just requires a stronger determination, focus and concentration.

...

Walking in Nature

Finding balance

Although an urban practice is possible, going to nature can be helpful and very nourishing. Henry Thoreau talks about retreating to a forest:

> *'I went to the woods because I wished to live deliberately,*
> *to front only the essential facts of life.'*

Let us take some time out of our lives to practice in nature; not necessarily on a mission to achieve something special, or go to a specific location, to make it to the top of a hill, count a certain number of steps, or make it to the end of a path. We go into nature, to be present.

When we go for a walk, remember Thoreau's observation after he had walked one mile:

'I am alarmed when it happens that I have walked a mile into the wood bodily, without getting there in spirit.'

Thoreau is describing the effects of mindlessness, where we travel bodily, yet our spirit or mind is elsewhere. When we walk mindfully, we bring our attention to the body. As we gain insight into how we can bring our mind into the body, we become balanced, unified, and integrated, feeling complete and whole. We appreciate where we are and can notice each moment as it passes.

Start on relatively flat terrain where you can relax, which doesn't require much physical effort and exertion, so that you can focus entirely on the practice. As you progress, be adventurous, take your mindful walking practice to different natural environments; not only will you experience all the benefits of the training, but you will come to have a heightened enjoyment of the natural location.

If you are feeling adventurous, try doing this practice alone in nature, to get the most profound insight. Alternatively, practice with a friend or small group, and take time to discuss your experience before and after.

...

There is no need to rush or push the process. Start to draw your attention into the body. Feel the earth against your feet.

Notice the different sensations that pass through your body.

Observe the flow of your breath, rising and falling.

Walk slightly slower than usual so that you can notice the movements in your body. As you start to become familiar with the process and relax, absorb into the routine and start to notice how the world appears through your senses; the trees, flowers, sounds of animals, the sensation of the weather, the temperature, and smells.

Notice and observe. We are not labelling anything or intellectualising the process.

We watch the rise and fall of all that appears to our senses.

Observe the experience from one moment to the next. Go with it and follow the flow.

One significant element of this training is that it helps to let go of the past and the future naturally.

You cannot intellectually grasp being in the present moment. As soon as you do, then you miss the moment, and it is gone.

Everything is impermanent and changing, moment by moment. Nothing can stop this process. You follow, relax and let go.

As humans, our egocentric view makes us relate to phenomena as though it is not changing. Everything feels real and substantial. If you engage in this practice and commit fully to it, then you can start to appreciate impermanence, and consequently let go of both the past and the future.

As you can see, in all of the nature around us, in each moment there is growth, abiding and dissolution.

Nothing remains the same. Gently focus. Let go.

Focus again. Let go.

Open.

Relax.

Focus a little more. Let go.

Open.

Relax.

Repeat.

You are not imposing anything on what is happening.
Step back and observe.

Bathe in each moment you spend in the natural environment.

Over time, your attention dissolves from your head into your body and moment.

During your walk, stop and practise mindful standing; take it all in and slow everything down.

Take the mindful walk for as long as possible.

When you are ready to finish your session, spend a short time determining to carry the awareness you established in your daily life.

❖

...

As we are discovering throughout this text, for our practice to develop there is no correct external environment. Initially, it may seem that we need to be somewhere calm and relaxing. In the beginning, this can help. However, as time progresses, we can practise in many places. It is not so much the location, but the way our mind relates to it that is significant.

...

Mindful Standing

A practical method to connect with the present moment

Standing is an underrated activity. Just recently, standing has become a little in-vogue, with research showing that standing each day is good for our health. There was a headline article published in the mainstream media in the UK, entitled, 'How sitting down is slowly killing us'.

Leading an extremely sedentary lifestyle is commonplace. We can spend the majority of our day static, sleeping, driving to work, sitting all day at the office, driving home, sitting down when we arrive home, and then sleeping again. Physical vocations are becoming rarer, with machinery and AI taking over many mundane tasks.

Vast swathes of society move to urban environments, where we work sitting in our offices, staring at screens all day. If we take public transport, there is often a rush for a seat when our train pulls into the station. The thought of standing for our entire journey seems like a punishment. If we are waiting in a hotel, restaurant, office, hospital, or going to see a doctor, we are usually told to sit and wait. 'Please have a seat.' Most of the time, without thinking, we will take it.

On train platforms across the world, where members of the public are standing to wait for their connection, most will be looking at their phones, as they are forced to stand. Perhaps even when we must wait for twenty-seconds for the traffic lights to change, as we are standing there, we check our phone. If we are having a drink, standing at the bar with a friend and they go to the bathroom, we may immediately get our phone out, distracting ourselves away from the present moment.

To stand and 'do nothing' may seem like sheer madness. Look at those trees standing still. Completely still for hundreds of years. Surely that is sheer lunacy – we must be busy and occupied all the time!

However, standing has many benefits, and not just from a health perspective. The practice of mindful standing is a helpful way to connect with the present moment; to live in the now.

'Not doing' may seem like it is something we are forced to do when we have to wait. Although waiting gives us the opportunity to stop, we can become wound up due to the tendency that we always have to be 'doing' something. The next time you have to stand and wait, take the opportunity to practice. Notice the initial frustration arising in your body and mind, let it pass.

The busyness of the day grinds to a halt, due to the red light, the queue, the self-service machine not working; start to learn how to enjoy these moments and transform them into opportunities to be mindful.

Even if we turn on the kettle, we could stand and wait next to it; however, we feel the need to go and do something else while it is boiling. Why? The distracted mind is always seeking novelty and change. If we are forced to wait for a split second, our mind becomes bored. The mind which craves excitement fears boredom. Standing and waiting can seem tedious and counterintuitive to the busy, distracted mind. Standing can almost be an activity to avoid at any cost. As I write and edit this book, I am sitting down, and I imagine that you are most probably sitting down as you read the book. So why not try standing up for a few moments?

Straighten your back. Allow your shoulders to drop. Bend your knees very slightly.

Place your hands on your stomach, around the level of your navel. The left hand placed on the right. Notice their movement.

Gaze on the floor around two metres in front of you.

Bring your attention to the hands placed on your stomach.

Curl your toes slightly and feel their sensation against the floor, then relax them.

Notice the sensation of your feet against the floor. Draw your attention to this moment.

Abide in the present, allow all thoughts from the past and future to subside.

Practising like this is how you train in mindful standing. Engage with this process for as long as you wish. Try variations of this training throughout the day. Even while you are standing, notice the movement of your clothes against your body at the level of your navel. Perhaps, if you are waiting at a pedestrian crossing for ten to twenty-seconds, instead of distracting yourself with your phone, enjoy connecting with the present moment, and just stand there.

...

There are so many opportunities during the day to be mindful. With creative thinking we can appreciate how little time is needed, and that we do not need to wait for the 'right conditions' to engage with our practice. Potentially, we can train in mindful standing twenty or thirty times a day.

We can use all the opportunities when we wait as reminders to train in mindful meditation. If it is just ten-seconds each time we stop, then that could be up to five minutes during the entire day. With these short practices, where we train little and often, an approach known in Japanese as 'Kaizen', we start to learn how to unwind the mind during our everyday life. Little and often, small increases in practice, will lead to excellent results as times passes.

...

Mindful Stretching

Short essential practices to help prepare for meditation

These practices can be engaged in before or after your quiet sitting practice, or half-way through if you sit in a long session. Alternatively, you can practise them through an entire session if your body feels too agitated to sit. You may find after engaging in mindful stretching that you are in a more concentrated state of mind to then practise meditation.

The key to these stretches and what makes them different from the usual physical activities we engage in is twofold:

1. We move exceptionally slowly.
2. We are fully mindful of each sensation.

We start these stretches with:

...

Mindful Standing

1. Stand and feel the present moment against your body.

2. Place your hands gently against the navel.

3. Gaze slightly ahead of you, keeping your eyes almost open.

4. Notice the sensation of the soles of your feet.

5. Relax your legs and bend your knees a little, so you are rooted in the ground.

6. Observe how your hands move naturally up and down, gently against your stomach. Stay with this movement for a minute or so.

Then engage with each of the following stretches, up to five times.

...

Mindful Arms

1. Stand with your arms resting by your sides.
   Let your palms face behind you.

2. As you breathe in, lift your arms up in front of you so that they are level with your neck.

3. Breathe out and let them drop down.

4. Engage with this process, slowly, gradually, and mindfully.

5. Repeat this stretch five times, gently and carefully.

...

Mindful Wings

1. Stand with your arms to your sides.

2. As you breathe in, lift them up in front of you, so they are level with your neck.

3. As you breathe out, allow your arms to go back as far as you can, and hold for a short time.

4. As you breathe in, bring your arms as far as you can in front of you, and hold for a short time.

5. Then as you breathe out, allow your arms to drop down to your sides in their original position.

6. Repeat this exercise five times.

Mindful Neck

1. Take this practice very gently.

2. Stand in the mindful standing posture. Ensure that your back is straight and shoulders relaxed.

3. Breathe in, tilt your head to the right side, slowly. Hold the stretch. Breathe out, and slowly tilt your head back to the centre.

4. Breathe in, tilt your head to the left side, slowly. Hold the stretch. Breathe out, tilt your head back into the middle.

5. Breathe in, tilt your head down towards your chest, slowly. Hold the stretch. Breathe out, tilt your head back into the middle.

6. Breathe in, tilt your head back towards your spine, slowly. Hold the stretch. Breathe out, tilt your head back into the middle.

7. Do this series of stretches three times.

8. Once you have completed this sequence, remain in the mindful standing posture for one minute, bringing your attention into your body and to your breathing.

...

Mindful Bend

1. Start in the mindful standing posture. Breathe in.

2. Then bend your back and body forwards, at a right angle to the floor.

3. Hold the stretch, and then as you breathe out, move back into the mindful standing posture.

4. Engage with this sequence five times.

...

Mindful Rock

1. Follow your breathing, while engaged in mindful standing.

2. Then bend your back and body forwards, allowing your arms to hang down.

3. While in the position, take a few breaths.

4. Then allow your arms to rock gently from side to side as you breathe naturally.

5. Stay like this for around thirty-seconds.

6. Then gradually come up to the mindful standing posture.

7. Repeat this process several times.

...

Mindful Knees

1. Start in the mindful standing posture.

2. Breathe in and raise your hands up above your head.

3. Breathe out and allow your knees to bend slightly.

4. Breathe in and straighten your knees slightly.

5. Breathe out and let your hands come down to your sides.

6. Repeat these movements five times, taking your time, slowly and mindfully.

Complete the session of mindful stretching with a mindful standing practice, connect with the present moment, and dedicate the training so that you can bring this mindful energy to your life.

...

Engage with these stretches as individual exercises, or use them before a sitting meditation. If you wish, work through the entire cycle of stretches as presented, or practise one or two of them. If you feel that your sitting practice has become a little stagnated, then these stretches can bring new mindful energy and freshness to your training. Try them out before a sitting meditation, and you will notice a difference.

...

Mindful Exercise

Finding your mindful zone

In my early teens, I was a keen cross-country and long distance runner, holding school records for the 1500 metres, and running for the county and city team. We would train during the winter months on Tuesday and Thursday evenings around the streets of Aston in Birmingham; sometimes we would engage in hill runs, using a location that had a steady, gradually incline. These are the most challenging types of hills to run, as the endpoint is often entirely out of sight. I looked ahead as I was striding out one evening and noticed a street light glowing; my mind just latched onto it. It started to draw me in. I could feel and observe my body underneath me, but the point of reference on the horizon was drawing and pulling me in.

I had an incredible sequence of moments that gave rise to mental clarity and focus, for a short time transcending the whole idea of running and time. Some athletes call this 'being in the zone'. Cyclists who take long distance rides at altitude sometimes describe having an almost transcendent experience, where body and mind are united, with no pain or effort; just clarity, focus and peace.

After ascending the hill, I became aware of the breathing; just the breath, I became the breath, and my body had almost faded away. At the time I did not tell anyone about it; at the age of fourteen, it is a little tricky to articulate this kind of existential awakening.

Exercise can be hard work, a strain, it can hang heavy on our mind as something that we need to do, and then when we do it, we just focus on getting to the end of it. There are plenty of distractions when we exercise to keep us away from the present moment. In busy gyms, there is a multitude of mirrors, television screens and loud music. This modern way of exercise gives our attention the opportunity to be in a million different places, other than the present moment. If our practice is strong enough, then, of course, we can transform all these distractions; however, when we first get started with mindful exercise, I recommend trying to reduce the number of distractions that surround you.

Below we are going to explore running, cycling and swimming, transfer the instructions accordingly to your chosen activity.

...

Running

Firstly, let us explore how we can take a mindful run.

As you put on your running kit, take your time.

Notice the breathing.

Become aware of the sensation of your clothes as you put them on your body.

When you put on your shoes, notice the moments as they come into contact with your foot. Be fully present as you tie your laces.

Observe the mind that wishes to rush. Let this pass and draw your attention gradually to the present moment.

Start in the mindful standing posture. Spend one minute bringing your attention into the body.

Go through the mindful stretching listed above.

Set a positive intention for your run. As you slowly start, bring your mind to the entire physical process, feel the sensation on the soles of your feet as they touch the floor, and notice your posture.

Observe the breath as it passes through your entire body. When you first start this practice, it is helpful to go into nature, or somewhere where there are not too many distractions that can interfere with or stop your training. As your practice develops, you will be able to adapt it to any environment.

As you get into your stride, keep taking points on the horizon to focus on, allow them to draw you in. Keep centred and come to the sensation and activity of the breath. Try not to let your mind become distracted, use the process of running and breathing to bring you back to the present moment.

If you want to experiment with the practice, try speeding up your pace, slightly faster than you usually go. Your mind may initially resist; let that pass, by coming to the breath.

Allow your mind to immerse entirely with the breath. Absorb and abide in each moment. Progress like this for as long as you wish.

When you are ready, bring your run to a close, do some mindful stretching, then mindful standing and finally conclude with a short sitting meditation practice. Notice the body and breath.

As the session concludes, allow yourself to make a gentle determination to continue with your practice in the future, you can even mentally set an intention and time to exercise again.

...

Through the power of our decision-making and focus, we can make great physical and mental progress. Practising meditation at the end of engaging in exercise can prove to be very powerful. We will notice a difference; our mind will feel sharper, more alert and energetic.

As well as being a great practice to help bring us into the moment, interestingly enough, mindful exercise can also help us to speed up if that is our intention. I tried the above practice on a ten-kilometre group run and managed to take ten minutes off a time previously recorded when running in a distracted, painful, 'oh I hope this will finish' type mindset. We slow down to speed up. We will discuss this more in the next chapter, where we will be exploring how to work mindfully.

...

Cycling

When you cycle, follow a similar method as presented above, trying to become one with the moment. Draw your attention into the present. With each spin of the wheel, allow yourself to become more centred.

As time progresses if you have a natural, relaxed, kind attention, the boredom that arises from not being distracted begins to calm and dissolve. By spinning with the breathing and embracing the sensations within the body, you will become entirely one with the bike.

In his prime, Eddy Merckx, the great Belgian cyclist, was said to be half man, half bike. He had obtained such focus and poise with his craft, leading him to become utterly dominant in his sport.

Try going on a long distance cycle ride, when you are not rushing somewhere, and give yourself an opportunity to experience this mindful awareness.

...

Swimming

If you swim regularly, you may have already been practising these techniques without noticing.

When you swim efficiently, bringing your attention to the stroke and breathing, then you have no option other than to observe the flow of breath.

Try to absorb completely into the breathing. If you have thoughts, distractions and competitive minds arising let them dissolve and bring your mind to the moment.

Become aware of the flow, the breathing, and each movement of your body.

When you see an excellent swimmer gliding through the pool, it almost looks effortless.

When you apply mindfulness to your swim, you can start to move towards a similar flow. As you focus on the breath, your body starts to relax, and you can adjust your posture accordingly.

When you are ready to complete your swim, float there for a short time, observing the rising and falling of your breath.

Let your worries, anxiety and distracting thoughts dissolve, as you breathe out and as you breathe in.

Bring your mind into the present moment.

...

There are so many sports that require us to have focus and concentration just before and during the action. Just spending a little time engaged in a mindful breathing practice can help us develop the clarity of mind needed at those times. Top coaches are using elements of mindful practice to help athletes become focused and present. Uniting body and mind will naturally encourage optimum performance. For a professional sportsperson, their primary intention is to win and be competitive. In this training, we intend to train our mind and bring peace to our world.

With a creative approach, we can begin to witness how our mindfulness practice can permeate into every element of our life. In the beginning, when we start to try and integrate our mindful training, we follow instructions and the process may not feel entirely comfortable. As time progresses, however, it will start to become more natural. Over time we become more skilled and confident, to the point where we are no longer conscious that we are practising.

Let us now explore how we can bring mindful meditation into the centre of our life with a mindful flow.

MINDFUL FLOW

*How we can enjoy bringing a
mindful flow to our life*

The Jedi talk about the force: 'May the force be with you.' Zen practitioners use the word 'Mu'. The New Age World refer to 'Energy'. Those who believe in a creator-universe talk about the 'Spirit'. Whatever word you wish to use, it is sure there is a way of living, breathing, talking and thinking that brings peace, calm and clarity into our lives.

Thus far we have explored a series of practices, which help to draw us into the present moment, increase focus and awaken our mind from its usual distractions. We have engaged in mindful sitting, mindful standing, mindful walking, and mindful exercise. In this chapter we are now going to see how we can apply mindful awareness to other parts of our life, thus empowering ourselves to transcend the everyday difficulties arising from worry and frustration.

We are going to establish a flow which will help us integrate mindfulness into the very heart of our existence.

I remember when I first met one of my meditation teachers, a Tibetan Buddhist monk, who had been practising for fifty-five years. When I saw him it was like beholding a wide, unobstructed, flowing river; it was incredible to see. It was as though he had no obstructions or obstacles to where he was going, what he was thinking or what he wished to accomplish, while also appearing to move quickly, he was actually moving very slowly. It was intriguing. He seemed to have a flow, a lightness of touch and energy, a spirit of peace.

We know the contrast between someone who walks into a room with a serene, calm mind and someone who walks into a room with an aggressive, agitated mind. You may see some signs and indications on their face or the way they are holding their body, but there is more than that. There is something invisible, untouchable, yet at the same time palatable.

Think of the last time you were angry:

How did you open and close the door?

How did you walk?

How did you cook and prepare food?

How did you interact with those around you?

Think about a time you were distracted:

How was your interaction with the world?

How were your conversations and communications; was there any satisfaction?

Did you make progress in any element of your life?

Think about a time you were engaged and mindfully focused:

How was your connection with the world?

How did you feel?

How did you walk and talk?

Imagine now, if you were fully mindful. If you were to bring, peace, reflection, and presence to each moment:

How would you open doors, stand and wait, walk, drive, talk, commute and spend money?

Can you imagine?

If you can imagine something clear enough, then in the future, you can make it a reality.

Consider Tim Peake, the famous UK Astronaut. Many children have the wish to be an astronaut; maybe they imagine that they are. The same was true for Tim Peake. He took steps to actualise what was in his imagination. He found out how to become an astronaut and then engaged in the appropriate physical, verbal and mental actions. During the training and build up to launch, he held that vision of himself. Although focused on the task at hand, he had an image of what he was to become. Then eventually he became what he had previously visualised.

How do we make something happen in our life? We firstly imagine it and believe it to be possible. If we can believe that it is possible to have a mindful awareness and a flow of peace and calm in our lives, then this will be the starting point to actualise this experience. We can lay down the burden of excuses, laziness and negative thinking that prevents our progress and learn how to take steps to bring our imagination into reality.

Mindful eating is a practical way to help us get started in bringing this training to life, functioning as a helpful reminder to practice. Eating is something that we choose to engage in, possibly many times each day. Even if we forget to eat when absorbed in an activity, it doesn't take long once we have completed what we have been doing to catch up with our eating habit.

In this next section, we are going to learn how we can prepare and eat food slowly, thereby bringing peace into our mind and health into our body.

...

Mindful Eating

Harmonious practices to bring
health to our body and mind

There is a restaurant called Noma in Copenhagen, which is regularly voted as the best in the world and has a waiting list of up to three months for a table. A meal there would cost in the region of £200 per person. The staff at Noma prepare each course with incredible care, creativity and artistic flair. If you have ever visited somewhere similar, you will know the feeling of having beautifully arranged food, in small portions.

In such an environment, we take great care to eat slowly. To be mindful of the taste, we slow down, so we can take in and savour each moment. We will have waited some time for the meal, and paid handsomely for it, so it will make sense to us to be mindful when we eat our food.

In our life already we have some familiarity with being mindful. We consciously choose to take care and attention, so let us now consider transferring this to eating. We are mindful if we feel that what we are engaged with has value. As a human, we have the potential to be mindful and if we train we can improve our ability and capacity.

If we mentally create the time and mind space, we can learn to turn our training on and start to go with a mindful flow. Initially, it may be a little stop/start, we begin to enjoy and may get distracted, almost dropping the flow and return to auto-pilot mode. We notice this and return to applying effort and attention to regain our focus.

In Buddhist meditation, they use the analogy of starting and maintaining a fire. We need first to establish the fire which takes time, effort, and energy. Initially, we keep a keen eye on the flames, encouraging it to stay alight as without special care it swiftly reduces in power. When the fire is finally blazing, we can then benefit from its heat, and step back from applying effort. It is the same when we are establishing a mindful flow within our life.

It will not occur naturally in the beginning, so we need to encourage our awareness, keeping a gentle non-judgmental eye on it. Gradually the strength of our training builds and blazes into our daily life, heating all our activities, and the people with whom we interact.

...

Let us first explore the preparation of the first meal of our day, breakfast, and how we can approach it mindfully. The key to success in all mindful practices is in the preparation, and this is where we will start with mindful eating.

If you are going to eat a meal mindfully, it makes sense to prepare your food with attention, and focus carefully on the preparation.

Are you present as you open the fridge? Do you notice how you are carrying your body and what your mind is doing?

Catch your mind trying to be busy, multitasking and rushing through the process, three or four moments ahead.

Try to engage in one activity at a time.

Single-tasking will help you to be present.

The busy, rushed, distracted mind wishes to do many things simultaneously, in the belief that this will speed up the process. This attitude can slow us down, as we can miss, forget what we are doing, become confused, and then leave a trail of mess behind us.

As you prepare your breakfast, just do it, be there, follow the process.

When you boil the kettle or heat the milk while making your drink, try just standing and taking a few breaths. Bring your mind and attention inwards and away from rushing and busyness.

Just be there.

Slow down the process of preparation, observe everything that is happening, listen to the sound of the water, and thoroughly enjoy all the sensations from moment to moment.

As you become more familiar with this practice, your mind will begin to penetrate into reality.

You will start to see deeper into your world, beyond the stress, and into its actual nature.

Is it possible to see the whole universe in a grain of sand? If it is, then we need to be fully and completely present when we are looking at that grain of sand. Although we live our life, we will continuously miss it if we always wish to be elsewhere. Where is the rushing, busy mind taking us?

Through gently coming to the present moment when we are eating, appreciation arises simply from having water and food. The positive, happy mind of gratitude will dawn within when we allow ourselves to eat mindfully. If we are present when we engage in our actions, then our everyday activities will no longer appear boring and bland. They will engage us and provide a continuous stream of satisfying moments.

...

Harmony, Respect, Purity, and Tranquillity

Gaining inspiration from the Japanese Tea Ceremony

The ancient Japanese tea ceremony originates and derives its inspiration from the Zen tradition of arts and movement. Through observing, or even engaging with this ceremony, we can witness the complete awareness of mindful flow in action. The whole process of preparing a cup of tea can take up to forty-five minutes. The tea ceremony helps the practitioner connect gracefully with their world, so there will naturally be warmth and openness.

With this practice, there is no need to rush, no aggression or desire, just a moment by moment appreciation of what is. Our actions become a moving art.

Initially, we can miss the point by buying into the external trappings of the ceremony – the special pot, cups, tea, even going to Japan – however, the real tea ceremony is taking place within our mind. The tea ceremony is an act of presence, an offering of our full existence to the world. We commit to each moment and allow the unravelling of the selfless mind.

The mindful flow goes far deeper than occasionally eating a raisin slowly. The practice can help us to transform and bring creativity into many of our daily actions. We have a slow dance of gratitude with the world around us, thus encouraging a lightness of touch, an open peacefulness.

We are here. Each breath and moment is a new opportunity to appreciate this. We pour our morning tea or coffee and stay with it, and we follow what is happening, fully present, but unattached. We taste, not because we need or deserve it, but only because that is the next step; as we taste, enjoy and immerse in the myriad of flavours.

While tapping into the moment, we can start to appreciate the interconnectedness we have with everyone and everything on the planet. This insight is available to us if we can learn to slow down. The connectedness of our world will appear to our mind if we take the time to look carefully at each moment. You are not only tasting the tea, but you are also tasting reality. You drink what you need, not what you want. Through enjoying just what you need, you are creating a beautiful passage through time.

There is a book about a Buddhist nun, Tenzin Palmo, called 'Cave in the Snow'. She described when she was on retreat sometimes having one slice of toast for breakfast. She would prepare the toast very slowly and eat only half of the one slice. She was not depriving herself but enriching her life with awareness. She consciously chose to start her day with mindfulness and not desire. Her breakfast was an extension of her meditation, an expression of her practice. To eat mindfully, remember your breath, the natural flow, your body, and the sounds around you.

The practices of mindful listening, mindful body and mindful breathing, which we have engaged in from the first three chapters, we now integrate into our activity.

As a child we were amazed much of the time, having new awakenings continuously. As our life progresses, our mind can become stagnant and aged with disinterested familiarity as we go about our daily routine, and we need to search further for those mesmerising experiences.

When we develop a mindful flow, we are starting to accept our unpolished selves and moments, and instead of seeking to make everything conform to our wishes, we embrace each moment. We cannot capture moments. The moment has gone as soon it arises. To awake to our life, we need to be present when the moments come.

There are billions of photos taken each day as we try to capture moments, keep and cherish them. Many people apply filters to their images, to make them appear mystical, historical or nostalgic. It is, however, impossible to grasp or seize the moment.

Our interpretation of the famous Latin expression 'carpe diem', 'seize the day', can potentially confuse. If we want to seize the day, we need to let go of it.

To help this, we try to approach our moments of eating and drinking with the four main principles introduced in the Japanese tea ceremony: Harmony. Respect. Purity. Tranquillity.

These concepts are not exclusively Japanese. We do not need to travel to the Far East to gain insight into them. They have merely been spelt out by this ancient tradition. They are available and accessible for everyone to practice, regardless of faith, background, education and social standing. Let us explore further how we can apply these four themes to our breakfast. Transfer the instructions to any food or drink of your choice.

As already mentioned try to practise alertness when you are preparing your breakfast.

The way in which you open the cupboard, how you look for the item, how you gather your utensils, how you open the fridge, how you take out the items, how you close the fridge and the way you gather all these items together.

If you are present and attentive, you will start to bring **harmony** into what you are doing.

Gather your attention and focus. Be in one place, one moment.

With the integration of your mind and body, you feel in harmony with what you are doing. No part of you wishes to be anywhere else but here.

If you are eating alone there may be a desire to turn on the radio, glance at the newspaper, switch on the television, phone or computer.

Just let this go, let this pass.

See what it is like to be in the moment, just eating and nothing else.

Your mind is in one place; where you are.

How can you eat your breakfast with **respect?**

If you check carefully, it is possible.

Respect is a humble mind, a mind of humility learning from each interaction that you have. It is open, ready to learn from everyone and everything.

The opposite of humility is deluded pride, where we feel there is nothing new to learn. We already know all about everything. We feel the need to elevate our self and rise higher and above others.

If you approach eating with respect, then you will honour the engagement and be able to appreciate where your food has come from, and be able to see that countless people have worked hard for you to enjoy it. Respect will keep you open to this insight; without it, the door will remain closed, and you will not be able to see the conventional reality of your world.

As you prepare your food, take the time to notice the smells and even the sounds that arise. Observe with respect. Remember those who have made it possible for you to enjoy the cereal.

Millions of people's hard work, dedication and sacrifice have been put into the ingredients of your breakfast, before you were able to enjoy it. The long line of cause and effect goes back as far as we can imagine. Approaching your food with respect allows gratitude and appreciation to arise.

Your respect is like a record player. The food is the record. Your attention is the needle. As you place the needle of your attention to the record of eating the food, it will naturally play the sounds of appreciation and gratitude.

There may be a temptation to rush the rest of the food. Try to keep a pure mind. You are not just feeding yourself; you are eating to fuel your body so that you can bring benefit to many people and contribute to peace within the world. This food will help sustain you.

Behind the practice is not 'I, I, I', but an appreciation of 'you, you, you'; so when we eat, it is not just a self-centred activity. With this approach, **purity** can start to pervade our mind.

You may be thinking: 'I just want to eat the damn food, I am hungry!' Sure, that is what we are getting to, through the whole of this section, we are looking at how we can just eat. Most of the time, when our mind wanders during eating, we are not actually eating the food, rather, in some way our distractions and busy thoughts are eating us, depriving us of a rich mindful engagement. They are telling us that we will have a fulfilling time in the future when everything is just right.

In reality, everything is just right, as it is, right now, if our mind accepts.

The fourth theme, **tranquillity**, arises when we accept the way that things are happening, without continually needing to tinker, improve and adjust.

There is a great Zen story which illustrates this acceptance. An esteemed monk came as a visiting teacher to a monastery. He gave inspirational teachings. Towards the end of the session, as he was walking out of the temple, one of the stewards helping with the smooth running of the event adjusted a picture on the wall that was slightly crooked, so that it was completely straight.

As the teacher walked by, he noticed this change. He readjusted it, so it was crooked again. There was a nervous laugh in the room, and he walked out.

Acceptance of what is will bring tranquillity to our life.

If your food arrives and it is not salty enough, do you need to add more salt? Not sweet enough? Could you possibly add the sweetener of awareness to your food, rather than more sugar?

Your practice of mindful eating can be worked on, cultivated, and developed over time, like all the practices presented in this book.

Eat what you need and then stop.

During the clear up and conclusion try to carry your presence and attention, thereby leaving no physical trace of your actions, so the next person who visits the space has a pleasant experience. As a result of being present, there will be no trail left behind you.

Naturally bring your attention to the present moment, not needing to yank it back. Kindly, gently, naturally, abide. Whatever it is you are doing reminds you to come home, to the present.

Allowing the busy multitasking mind to dissolve.

Whenever you finish a meal, having practised like this, determine to carry the mindful awareness you have developed into your daily life.

...

After reading this section, make the intention that the next time you eat or drink to shine your attention onto the present moment and to and incorporate the four elements of harmony, respect, purity and tranquillity.

Make an effort to slow down and enjoy just eating and drinking during your busy day. Establish the habit of pausing and taking a few breaths before you start. Bring yourself into the present. Use your senses to interact with the food. In between mouthfuls, put your knife and fork down, take a few breaths, and then take another mouthful. In the live classes, when I introduce mindful eating, we use a raisin and then a small chunk of chocolate, which is proving to be a very popular session.

I set up a resources section on the meditationinschools.org site, to bring practices to students and staff across the world, and the 'Mindfulness and the Art of Chocolate Eating' guided practice, has become one of the most popular downloads. It can be a fun way to introduce mindful principles to children. Take a look when you have time, try some of the practices and if you live or work with children consider sharing with them. As with all the practices presented here, I encourage you, once you have tried them for yourself and gained confidence, to then share with those around you.

...

Mindful Work

Improving mental health, well-being, focus, and productivity

In my work of teaching mindful meditation, I have had the opportunity to introduce mindful thinking to large corporations, charities, small businesses, universities, schools, and nurseries. Sometimes I will give a one-off taster session or introduction, and other times a series of classes, covering the themes introduced in this book delivered both live and online. It is encouraging to see that many organisations are now keen to explore the benefits of mindfulness.

There is a new mindset growing around the benefits of mindful training in the workplace for employees' emotional well-being and personal development, and in general for the well-being and progress of organisations as a whole. Mindful instruction is often introduced en masse; however, for the effects of mindful practice to be experienced first-hand, it is self-motivated individuals who need to step forward and practically engage with the training. You cannot force a person to be mindful. When Buddha initially taught he only taught those people who wanted to hear and practice.

A mindful workplace arises from individuals practising. Just one person practising in a company or school can have a profound effect on their peers, and the company as a whole. Let us explore how we can transform our mind at work and then the workplace environment. Firstly, let us look at our approach to work. Depending on your circumstances, apply the following instructions to study, parenting, voluntary work, or work around the home. Please adapt the instructions creatively to your circumstances.

Are we working to live, or living to work? Alternatively can we 'be' in each moment of our life and not see any difference between our working and non-working life? We may reflect that it is tricky to abide in the present moment when we do not particularly want to be there. The rush to work, the rush home from work, the seemingly never-ending commute. We may have to travel and work each day for the majority of our adult life.

Many people must commute two hours or more each day. Accommodation prices in city centres are rising continuously, forcing people further out into the suburbs. If we wish to have awareness when we are working, then it can be helpful to learn how to integrate mindfulness into our commute. Our commute can be an opportunity to practise mindful sitting, mindful standing, and mindful walking. It is an unrivalled opportunity also to practice the mindful heart.

As with all the mindful practices, it is helpful if, in our system already that day, we have some momentum which has come from our practice of mindful sitting. We abide in the present and gently wake to everything around us: people's expressions, shapes of clouds, shades of colour, noticing the small details. We open kindly to the lives of those around us, raising our awareness and attention. We try relating to others potential, not their apparent faults.

Do we need to look at our phone all the way to work? Take the opportunity to unwind and enjoy the journey, get into a relaxed zone. Set your positive intention for the day. Gather your energies, as opposed to distracting them.

Of course, phenomena such as phones, computers, and newspapers are not distracting in themselves; it is the way that we choose to interact with them that governs whether they are distracting.

There can be a rush to be somewhere else other than where we are, a rush to get to work, a rush to get through work, and then a rush to get home. In this hurry, there are thousands of life moments that we could be embracing which are arising and dissolving right in front of us. By merely turning our mind and attitude to what is happening we can start to connect and enjoy all the benefits of being mindful.

As a tool to bring our attention to the now, we can use our breath. The breath is our anchor to the present. We can engage in facsimiles of all the mindful breathing practices. If we are on public transport or waiting, with our eyes open or closed, we can tap into the present. The effect of integrating mindfulness into our commute is that we arrive at work with a focused, calm, sharp mind that has been recharged by our training. Our mind needs to rest and also be empowered, and the way to do this is by tapping into the present moment as often as we possibly can.

Here are a few tips as to how we can be mindful during our drive to work (adapt if you take public transport):

Before turning on the ignition, take a few mindful breaths and set your intention for the day.

'I am going to bring mindfulness and peace into my day and share this with all the those around me.'

Feel your body on the seat and feet against the floor.

Relax your shoulders and keep an upright posture.

When your journey is slowed down at a traffic light or by roadworks, use the waiting period to focus on your breath, allow yourself to become completely alert.

In the live classes when I was teaching this subject, one man exclaimed: 'Surely it would be dangerous to practise mindfulness at the wheel.'

If we check carefully, it is the opposite. It is because we do not practise attentiveness, accidents on the road arise.

When we are multi-tasking, using our phone, having a lively conversation, or listening to loud music, then our mind can be distracted.

If drivers were to practise mindfulness, nearly all highway accidents would stop.

The thought that it is dangerous to be mindful when we are driving is a misconception, which arises from the view that mindful meditation is an action that spaces you out and removes you from reality. In truth, it helps you to become fully aware. Remember the definition of being mindful, introduced at the beginning of the book: an open, non-judgmental awareness of the present.

If you are driving and someone cuts you up, or you feel frustration arising from how slowly the traffic is moving; try to notice these emotions as they arise.

Instead of becoming the frustration, and letting it take over the body, allow it to pass, like a cloud in the sky.

Of course, it is simple to say and understand intellectually, but the practice is not easy if we have no familiarity. With regular training, however, it is possible.

Start to see the frustration arising out of the corner of your mind.

Notice the stress manifesting in your body, and recognise the tightness in your hands against the steering wheel.

Noticing with openness is a powerful way to reduce the tension in your mind, and will naturally bring you to the present moment.

You do not want to be anywhere other than where you are; this is it, this is your life.

...

Many issues can arise in the workplace. Personality clashes with colleagues, contractors or suppliers, continuous deadline pressure, competitive tension over promotions, feeling overworked and not appreciated, having to deal with disappointment after having high expectations, or just an underlying, niggling, discontent. Your practice of mindfulness can help you deal with, and sometimes conquer, these issues.

When you arrive at work, before rushing into your day, pause, take a moment to gather your thoughts, and renew your intention. The pauses advised in this book may appear as though they are slowing us down – we have things to do! It can be frustrating having to stop. If you check carefully, through pausing, you can begin to tap in and access the present moment. In this way, you are starting to prepare the ground for the house of a mindful life that you can enjoy living in. Pausing like this is the foundation of your practice, and gives you the space, time and opportunity that you need to breathe.

...

As you go into your workplace, check your posture, your intention. Notice if your mind drifts. Try to refresh and view each moment as new. If you slip into autopilot, you will start to miss the moment and draw closer to becoming a machine than a being. Try to make breath-checks regularly through the day. It may be just for three-seconds. Take little pauses, where you just breathe.

Take a breath-check:

While you wait for the internet to load.

Before you take a sip of morning coffee.

When you open an e-notification.

When you are about to press send on an email.

As you feel frustration arise towards a colleague.

As often as you possibly can, take a breath-check.

Also, try to take the opportunity to have a tea break, you deserve a break during the day and are legally entitled to one. Be creative in your life and look out for the opportunities to have a breath-check. Tap into the present moment, and allow this process to recharge your mindful flow.

Step back during each sip of your drink, pause and breathe.

Turn away briefly from the computer, pause and breathe.

Step right away from your computer and phone; have a break, let yourself breathe for a while.

Just like a smoker does when they go outside, but now you go out and breathe in some fresh air!

If you find yourself clock-watching, pause, take a breath, let the time remind you to be present instead of waiting for the future to come.

If you are frustrated by overhearing somebody's conversation, instead of stewing in the negativity that has arisen, take a breath and develop the wish for them to be free from their problems, difficulties and negative states of mind.

Remember to draw yourself into the present moment, as often as you can. Every twenty to twenty-five minutes take the time to break, even if it is just for a short time. Turn away from the screen, even step away for a few moments, enjoy the space and return with renewed energy. On the journey home from work see if you can follow the commute instructions presented above, and start to establish the tendency of drawing yourself into the present moment, so it becomes a natural habit,

Now, as you are reading this, take a breath-check, notice the inhalation and exhalation. Pause for a short time.

Our work does not have to be a chore or grind if we can be fully present and commit wholeheartedly to each moment. It is not so much what we do, but the way that we do it.

Mindful Sweep

Adopting a skilful, mindful approach to our daily activities

I remember my dear grandfather always saying how much he enjoyed washing up. He engaged in the process very slowly and mindfully. He never mentioned the word 'mindful'. Our chores can easily be elements of our life that we quickly sweep out of the way, so we can progress forward to what appears to be the more important elements of our life. With a skilful approach, our chores can provide us with the opportunity to practise mindfulness and draw our attention to the present moment.

Engaging in our chores with mindfulness can help us to unite the body and mind, and learn to see through the stress that can so often take over our head. As mentioned previously, within Zen monasteries, some of the most esteemed positions are the cleaner, kitchen worker, and gardener. Positions which, within our society, have a lowly status, and to which maybe we as individuals do not aspire. If we have the resources we may even outsource these jobs, so we have the time to engage in what we may see as more meaningful activities.

Every chore, however, whether it is ironing, washing up, laundry, cleaning, cooking, or vacuuming, can give us an excellent opportunity to slow down, to bring our self into the present moment and practice being mindful. As we engage with an activity in a mindful way, we come into the here and now, the stress from thinking about the future, and the past, naturally dissolves away. These seemingly mundane activities become transformed, with our mindful attention.

We can take inspiration from the famous Buddhist monk, Lam Chung, who spent all day sweeping the temple courtyard, while other monks were meditating and studying. He engaged in his work with great care and awareness, and gradually gained very high realisations.

...

Mindful Net

How being online and sitting at a computer can strengthen our mindful practice.

In general, as time progresses, we are spending more of our lives online, working and communicating via technology. Many people will spend nearly all day looking at and working on a computer. We live in a digital age, and increasingly technology takes a central position in our life. There is a school of thought that states that we need to retreat from technology and computers if we are to make progress along the mindful path. Of course, technology can be distracting. However, as to whether something distracts us or not depends on our intention and the way that we interact with it, not the object itself. There is no such thing as an inherently, distracting phenomenon.

If we are skilful, being online and sitting at a computer can strengthen our mindful practice. It all depends upon our approach. In this section, I am going to present you with a few tips that will encourage mindful awareness when we are interacting with technology.

...

Taking Breaks

How to keep a clear head when working

One practice that I sometimes use when working on a computer is to take a break every twenty-five minutes. I set a timer on my phone and start working. When the timer goes off I turn away from the computer, perhaps get up and make a drink, do some stretching, or take a short walk around the room, just for four to five minutes. Also, during this short break, I will look at doing a little breathing meditation, even if it is only for thirty-seconds. Then I go back to my desk and start again for another twenty-five minutes. This practice refreshes my mind, keeps my attention clear, and brings me into the moment. Even if you are busy and do not want to break away from your desk, it will help your output, so that you can be more efficient and influenced by mindful awareness.

...

Sending Compassion

Encouraging harmonious communication

When we are using our computer sending and receiving messages, it is sometimes easy to forget that on the receiving end of our correspondence is an actual human being with feelings and emotions. The tone of our communications and the intentions behind them can influence the mood of the receiver. For example, when we send an email, we could wish that the receiver has a good day and can find meaning in their life. We send our positive energy with the mail. If we can remember to do this, then there will be beneficial consequences for both us the sender, and the person who reads the email.

Even in the email asking, 'how was their weekend' or wishing them a 'good day' can make a difference to the interaction and create a warm basis for the relationship. We may find ourselves on the receiving end of a challenging email and feel an instinctive, defensive, emotional response arise. We can observe the feeling and physical tension that builds up, watch, take a breath, step back and let it pass. Pause for a while and consider a positive, constructive response that can benefit both you and the receiver of your email.

In the past when we would correspond via letter, during the time that it took to compose and write the communication, find an envelope and stamp, and walk to the post box, we would have potentially been able to let go of the frustration in our body and mind, and not even have sent the mail. In fact, advice was often given to write a letter to get the frustration out of one's system, but then not post it.

Communication is rapid, which can be helpful, but in another way can cause issues. Due to reacting immediately with defensive thoughts the person on the receiving end then has to receive and process these emotions. As human beings, we have the capacity for cultivating emotional intelligence and have harmonious communication with everyone; we can utilise our mindfulness practice to encourage this.

...

Completing Tasks and Reducing Distraction
Defragmenting our mind for heightened concentration

One issue for many workplaces is not absenteeism, but presenteeism; we are at work, but only just. If our mind is distracted and tired, it is not easy to focus on the task at hand, making relatively simple jobs take much longer than necessary.

Therefore, it can be helpful to set ourselves small tasks and try to complete them before starting the next one. When we finish the task, we take a short break, feel happy with what we have accomplished and set our intention for what we are going to do next. When our mind is tired and not fresh, it is more prone to distraction. Noticing distraction we let it pass, check if it is necessary or just a habit, and either refocus or take a break.

Having social media and news sites open can also fragment our attention and cause a sense of continuous, mild, agitation and distraction to be the underlying flavour of our working life. One significant element of limiting our use of these sites is that when we come to engage with them we will have more enjoyment and focus and their presence in our life can be helpful.

...

Wholehearted

Enjoying each moment, wherever we are

If we spend a considerable amount of time working at the computer, it makes sense to be there, and not to wish our life away. If we are not happy with our work we have two practical options to be satisfied: change our attitude, or change our job. We use our physical and mental energy to engage with one of these two encouraging actions.

The clock-watching approach, waiting for 5pm, and Friday to arrive, does give us something to look forward to, but means we miss many moments of our life. What about trying to immerse ourselves and delight in each moment of work?

We try not to get sucked into negative thinking and instead give ourselves to each moment of our life. If we can approach our work wholeheartedly, we will be able to bring our mindful awareness to other elements of the day: at home, at leisure, and while we travel. In this way our mindful training is organic and holistic, reaching all parts of our life.

...

Adjusting our Posture

Heightening creativity and innovation at work

During our working day, we may feel a little mentally and physically drained; sometimes adjusting our posture can have the positive effect of freshening our mind. It can help to just gently straighten our back, relax our shoulders, and loosen our hands from time to time.

Try placing both feet on the ground and notice the sensation of the earth. Become aware of the breath and its journey around the body. Looking away from the screen and taking in what is happening around us, even for a few moments, can be beneficial. Adjusting our posture allows our mind to become broad and expansive, helping our mental and physical health, bringing heightened creativity and innovation to our work.

When I lived in Nepal, I would visit an Englishman who had been sentenced to twenty years within the central prison in Kathmandu. We would share time and stories together. The last words that he said to me as I was walking away from the prison were, 'always keep your mind on the horizon'. Those words have stayed in my heart since then.

See if you can keep your mind expansive while working, helping your mindful training flourish and benefit many people.

...

Mindful Mobile

Using our mobile phone to become more mindful

If you are out in public now then there is most probably someone in your eye-line who is on their mobile phone. The mobile has almost become part of our body, and we can spend many hours each day interacting with it. It is now a significant part of life and, for many alive today, they will not have known a life without one.

Of course, it can be helpful for our mindful practice to take a complete break from our mobile. From time to time, leave it at home, go out for a walk, spend a day at work, or have a night out, where you are mobile free. Deliberately have time away from it.

As mentioned previously though, it is not mobile phones which are distracting; they are just flashing bits of metal. It is how we relate to them which makes them a distraction. Are we in control of our phone or is our phone in control of us? If we are skilful, our mobile phone can make us more mindful. There are a series of small practices that we can integrate into our lives that will help us to be more mindful while we are on our phone.

When our phone rings or notifies us, the usual response is immediately to see what the update is. A useful mindful practice that we can engage in when we first become aware of the notification is to bring our attention to the breath for a few moments. The notification is reminding us to become present and mindful. A short while later we then check the phone. If we can remember this simple practice, we will be able to create pockets of peace throughout our day.

Usually, with any physical phenomenon, we have a mental association. For example, when we see, think, or feel our phone, we can think about social media, dating, or a game that we enjoy. As we start to use our mobile to remind us to become mindful we can associate awareness and presence with it, so it brings us into the moment, instead of functioning as a tool to take us into a virtual vacuum.

When we are browsing through our phone, we can still maintain an awareness. We try to keep a connection with the breath and body. During our scrolling, we can keep an eye on our mind, watching thoughts and distractions as they arise, and then let them pass. Notice when the mind starts to become agitated and distracted; observe this process and let the distractions pass. If we are not conscious, our phones can drain our time, attention, and focus. Through becoming skilled in this practice, we will preserve much of our precious, human time.

Prolonged use and distracted habits can begin to rewire the brain, losing and weakening our valuable attention span. In the same way, learning mindful meditation techniques, and integrating them, can function to rewire our brain and mind, encouraging a strengthening of memory, focus, and attention.

We now have many mindfulness apps that can help us get started with a meditation practice. I designed the Mindspace app for practising mindful meditation on the go. We begin with one-minute exercises and gradually build up our capacity.

...

Through following the above training, we can initiate the process of bringing peace and calm into our day. Try to keep a positive intention to practice, even if it is just for a short time. Gently engage in the training. Move forward by encouraging yourself and build on the small moments of mindfulness. In this way, gradually your mindful awareness will start to flow naturally.

MINDFUL SLEEP

*How to fall asleep peacefully
and wake up smiling*

Sleeping mindfully will transform our lives. The quality of our sleep determines the quality of our waking life, and the quality of our waking life will determine the quality of our sleep. The following practices will help us to gain experience of a mindful sleep and give us the opportunity to rest deeply.

There is a wealth of information available on the subject of sleep. Most of it focuses on the time just leading up to sleep and the quality of the external environment during these moments. Advice and suggestions are given for a change of duvet, mattress, pillow or bed. Exploring different ways to ventilate the room and change the lighting mood. Perhaps even tips on how to purchase a special sleeping outfit.

One essential factor that is missing from most of the instructions and sleep advice in the public domain is the discussion around our mood and mental state during the waking day.

If we can train in all the practices mentioned in this book, then we will be giving ourselves a good opportunity to fall asleep peacefully. Processing and letting go of our stress, while on the move throughout the day, means we can sleep without carrying it into our dreams.

The final state of mind that we fall asleep with is the culmination of all the minds we have had during the day. If we can learn to relax and unwind the mind when we are awake, then this will help us to fall asleep, peacefully and mindfully. If we allow our mind to be wound up during the day and let it be at the whim of distraction, it is unrealistic to then be able to expect to fall asleep straight away and have a peaceful, calm night.

Appreciating that the process of having a mindful sleep is a holistic, organic process that depends upon our other mindful practices, will ensure that we have the best possible opportunity to benefit from this training.

...

Calm Sleep

How to fall asleep peacefully, and then how to get back
to sleep if we wake up in the night

This practice will help us to fall asleep with a calm, relaxed mind.
A lady came to one of my classes and was asking for advice on
how she could improve her sleep. I taught her the calm sleep
practice. The following week she came back and told me that she
had managed to cure her twenty years of insomnia with this
method. Here is the training that I shared with her.

Settle into your bed. Lie down on your back and gently place your
hands on your stomach, around the level of the navel.

Gradually draw all your attention into your body, try to notice and
be attentive to any sensations. Move the energy and awareness
that has built up in your head, down into your body.

Draw your mind towards the hands on your stomach. Place your
attention here and have this as the focal point for your concentration.

Try to anchor your mind here. If it wanders back up your body
into your head and out of the room, then use your awareness of
your hands on the stomach to come to the present moment.

Start to notice how your hands rise and fall in time with your
breathing.

Your hands move naturally on their own, due to the rising and
falling of your breath. Simply follow the process.

Stay with this gentle movement until you are ready to sleep.

As you are about to fall asleep, move into a more comfortable posture, perhaps on your side or front.

Then enjoy your calm sleep.

❖

...

If the last moment of mind that we fall asleep with is calm, then this naturally affects our dream state. If our dreams are peaceful, then we can have a restful sleep, and rise refreshed and alert, ready to enjoy the new morning with mindful awareness.

The beauty of this first sleep practice is in its simplicity. To have a mindful sleep we need a solution that is straightforward. If we have a practice that is too elaborate and complex, then this may have the opposite effect and function to keep us awake, due to our mind spinning with the technicalities of practice.

...

Mindful Night

Looking at the mind and body before sleep
while using the sleeping lion posture

How can we be more mindful when we are dreaming and in a state of deep sleep? As mentioned above it is essential to practise the mindful training during our daily life so that we are more used to being in the present moment, and skilled at being able to let go swiftly of stress and anxiety.

What can we do just before we drift off with our mind and body to ensure a mindful sleep?

Buddha himself encouraged a posture for sleep, and it was also the posture that he adopted when he passed into Nirvana. There are some statues of Buddha in this posture which you may have seen in Thailand. The posture is known as the sleeping lion posture. It is suitable for keeping a clear, alert mind before we fall asleep, and is healthy for our internal organs, as they have no pressure on them overnight, from the weight of our body.

Please lie outstretched on your right side. Make sure that you are warm and comfortable.

With your head rested on a pillow, place your right hand under your right cheek.

Rest your left hand along the left side of your body, relaxing into the posture. Bend your legs slightly.

Gradually start to gather your attention into the centre of your body.

Follow the sensation of your breathing for a short time and bring your attention into the heart chakra (located in the exact centre of your body, in the middle of your chest). Try to bring all your awareness to this location.

Visualise a sesame seed of light here, recognise that this is your peaceful potential and all your good, positive energy. Rest your mind and attention at this point for a short time.

Observe your mind as you start to relax. Notice as it becomes more subtle. Be aware of its dissolution as you begin to drift into sleep. Watch as your mind gradually loosens its hold on your external life and enters your inner world.

You may be able to fall asleep in this posture, or if not choose to move into a more familiar position.

Sweet dreams!

Usually, when we fall asleep, we lose complete awareness of our consciousness. Here we are retaining our alertness and with some practise can start to enjoy a subtler level of mind before sleep. The effect of this practice is that we will have a more mindful state as we fall asleep. In the Tantric meditation texts, there are more profound practices that we can do once we have gained proficiency with this method.

...

Deep Dreams

The importance of meditation before sleep

Establishing a formal meditation practice through our life will naturally influence our sleep and dreams. Our dreams can teach us about our life. If we have a clearer, more focused mind, we can start to remember our dreams and learn from them.

Falling asleep in an agitated state, can influence our dreams, and make us wake with a feeling of tiredness and exhaustion, even though we may have slept through the entire night. We have discussed earlier in the book the importance of engaging in a morning meditation practice. If we can practise at this time, we are giving our self the best opportunity to maintain a mindful awareness during the day.

To enhance and encourage a mindful sleep another good time to practise meditation is right at the end of our day, just before we sleep.

The Dalai Lama, one of the most famous meditators in the world, has two main meditation times during the day, one at the beginning, when he has just woken, and one at the end of the day, just before sleep. If we can establish this beneficial, mindful habit, then it can help us to have a more restful night's sleep, wake up calmly, practise again in the morning and then head into a mindful day.

Establishing this habit will have a beneficial effect on both our waking and sleeping life, providing us with the basis for greater insight into our dream state. For mindful practice to have a transformative impact, then a holistic approach is essential.

At the live classes that I teach sometimes, I joke with the attendees about rushing mindlessly to a mindfulness class, to squeeze one hour of practice into our week, in the hope that it will somehow miraculously transform the rest of our life. One hour is better than nothing: but it is not enough to gain the insight necessary to maintain awareness in our sleep. For this, we need to bring awareness to all parts of our day.

Buddha stated, 'You should know that all phenomena are like dreams' and encouraged those who wish to be happy, peaceful and lead a meaningful life, to abide in a dream. This instruction helps us let go of our world and gain an insight into our reality. Through Buddhas practice, he awoke from the sleep of confusion. One of the most effective ways to help us 'wake up' is to appreciate that our world is more dream-like than it seems. If we can start to let go of our waking world, then when we sleep, we can begin to have some insight and awareness into our dream state. Our mind has incredible power and potential; start a daily meditation practice and begin to appreciate this first-hand.

Before sleep, disconnect from all technology, and engage in a mindful practice, perhaps sitting up in bed or on the side of your bed, on a chair in your bedroom, or on the floor next to your bed. Allow your mind to settle and relax with your breath, gently process the day and allow peace to arise in your mind.

...

Compassionate Sleep

Growing our potential during sleep

By establishing the mind of compassion before we drift off, we can transform our sleep from a neutral experience to a positive and compassionate one. We can do this in formal meditation, sitting up in our bed, or we can practise as we are lying down, in one of the postures presented above, the lion posture or the mindful hands' posture.

Reflect briefly on the wish that you have to be free from problems and difficulties.

Allow the heartfelt desire for yourself to be free from these issues to develop.

Try to hold this state of mind for a short time.

Think about those who are currently close to you, friends, family, work colleagues, and neighbours; reflect how they also wish to be free from problems and difficulties, but as human beings have to encounter much uncertainty and confusion.

Allow the compassionate mind to develop in your heart that wishes they can be free from their difficulties and find freedom in their minds. Try to hold this mind for a short time.

Extend this mind of compassion outwards, so it begins to include all the people in your area; hold this briefly.

Then extend the mind of compassion further, to everyone in your town, city, country, world, and universe.

Try and allow your compassion to reach as many people as you can imagine.

Hold the wish that everyone may find peace and happiness, and discover methods to solve their daily problems; gradually allowing the mind of great compassion to arise.

Stay with this compassionate mind for as long as you can, relaxing into it. Allow your mind to rest with this compassion.

Determine to hold this mind of compassion through your sleep and when you wake to be influenced by it, both in the morning and throughout the new day.

See if you can fall asleep, with this incredibly positive intention.

Going to sleep with the mind of compassion will flavour our dreams and influence the state of mind that we have when we rise the next day.

Waking Up Smiling

Encouraging happiness before sleep and upon rising

Let us now explore a wonderful, positive practice that we can enjoy both as we fall asleep and as we rise, uplifting our mind and protecting us from unhappiness and negativity. We can engage in the contemplation in a formal meditation posture, sitting up in bed or on the side of our bed, or we can reflect as we are lying down on our bed.

Consider your day, mentally review what has happened with the mind of gratitude.

Develop appreciation. Process the day with gratitude, reflecting on the opportunities and kindness you have received.

Allow the mind of gratitude to arise.

So that you can generate this mind, a general contemplation is enough; you do not need to go into detail about any specific event.

You can even develop gratitude for the fact that you have a bed to sleep in and shelter over your head.

If it helps, try to think of three things you have to be grateful for from the day.

Then three things you have to be grateful for right now.

Then three things you can feel grateful for about tomorrow's day.

When the mind of gratitude arises clearly in your mind, try to hold it and allow your mind to be influenced by it, as though your mind and gratitude become one. There is no gap between you and gratitude. You become this precious mind.

When the mind of gratitude arises, try to hold it and take it to bed with you, carrying it into your sleep. As you fall asleep, intend to rise in the morning and continue with your gratitude practice.

When you rise, immediately bring your attention to the breathing.

Please focus on the breath and observe how it enters and leaves your body. Think and feel in your heart:

'How wonderful I am still alive and breathing. I now have the entire day ahead of me. I am not going to waste my time. I am going to use it to develop gratitude and appreciation.'

If we can think like this, then we start the day with a positive mind and all our actions will have the potential to be influenced by this emotion. This training can flavour our mind with gratitude throughout the day up to the point when we fall asleep again, thus affecting our sleep and dreams, and this will then again in-fluence how we rise. With gratitude, we create the habit of a life-time. The power of our grateful intention will uplift our entire life. A gratitude habit will influence our emotions, moods, and relationships, bringing an upbeat, warm positivity to our mindful practice.

Through learning these methods, we will eventually be able to guide ourselves, without needing to read or listen to instructions. This will empower us, and give depth to our training, so we can feel confident to engage with it wherever we are, at any time.

MINDFUL HEART

Meditations to improve our relationships

Thus far, we have explored a series of practices that can strengthen our mindful awareness. If we engage with them regularly, they can help us to connect with a simple, more peaceful existence, guiding us into the present moment so we can have an enjoyable passage through life. In this chapter, we are going to take our training deeper by bringing mindful awareness to our relationships.

Our everyday happiness and well-being depend upon the quality of our relationships. If our interactions with others are satisfying and peaceful, we can have deep contentment and happiness. Practitioners discover, when starting a mindful practice, they can maintain some presence and awareness of the present moment when they are alone, but when they come to interact with others, they can swiftly lose their mindfulness.

The key to progressing and integrating our training is learning how to maintain our mindful awareness in daily life, especially with our relationships. The mindful heart practices provide us with a series of reflections and meditations that enable and empower us to integrate our training when we interact with others. Firstly, we learn to maintain a presence of mind when we are with our friends, family members and work colleagues, then we can also cultivate a mindful heart attitude, that can help enhance and improve these relationships, so they become meaningful and satisfying.

When we encounter difficulties with our relationships, it may seem as though it is the other person who needs to change or alter their behaviour. Over the course of these next pages, we can start to discover how our world and relationships will change when our mind, attitude, and intention change. Learning to adjust our mind and its perception of others can start to alter the world that appears to it.

Within the Buddhist tradition, they describe different levels of mind, from gross through to very subtle. When they talk about the subtle mind, they often point to the area around the centre of the chest: which is where our heart chakra is located. Concerning the mindful heart, we are referring to this. In our culture, if somebody is kind and has a loving nature, we proclaim that they have a 'good heart'. This 'good heart' is what we are looking to grow and encourage with this training. The warmer and more positive our heart is, the more satisfying our relationships will be.

...

Equanimity

Developing a balanced mind

Learning to cultivate a balanced, stable mind is the foundation for all the mindful heart practices; therefore we begin with the practice of equanimity.

Equanimity helps to balance our heart and mind through developing a warm, friendly feeling towards those around us. We begin extending this feeling to the people we interact with on a daily basis, then we include those whom we see and hear in public life, and finally to those whom we have not yet met.

The method of cultivating equanimity is to focus on the good qualities of others, which results in then having a friendly and positive attitude towards them. Equanimity is a balanced mind which allows a liking and encourages a feeling of warmth towards others.

When we meet somebody, we may have an immediate liking for them. For other people, we can take an instant dislike, while for most, we may have neutral feelings, neither liking or disliking. This neutral mind is quite common, and one of the reasons why much of the time our mind and life can have a 'neutral' feeling about it.

In our world, there are many people we have no particular interest in and have no feelings for, currently to us they are strangers. Equanimity begins the process of cultivating positive, new emotions towards those we previously did not include.

With the mindful heart, when we interact with others, we can start to notice the neutral emotions that arise. Instead of just following the habitual feelings that come into our mind towards others, we cultivate a positive warmth, through focusing on their good qualities. With equanimity, we keep our interactions beautiful and straightforward, generously extending positive thoughts and feelings towards others.

Our mind is often imbalanced, feeling close to a few, distant from others and indifferent towards many. With equanimity, we proactively begin to extend a warm liking to others by seeking out their good qualities and potential. Let us engage in a practice that can help us to get started with this training. Remember to be patient with yourself and this method and try to include as many people as you can.

It is natural to have challenging relationships in our life, and it is unrealistic to expect to solve these straight away. It is for this reason why I always encourage in the mindful heart classes that I teach to start this training slowly, working with more comfortable relationships, to begin with, and gradually, as our inner strength and capacity grows, to extend our practice further.

Begin by observing the sensation of your breathing.

Spend a short time gathering your awareness into the present moment. Settle your mind and look inwards.

Recall all the people in your life: friends, family, colleagues, neighbours; gradually extend the visualisation to all the people you have ever met.

Imagine they are next to you. Reflect on the positive; how all these people have good qualities and potential for growth.

Instead of focusing on their faults, try to bring to mind their good qualities.

Try to bring equanimity to mind, a balanced feeling within your heart, a warm liking of others.

Start with those who you are currently close to, and slowly build.

When the feeling of equanimity arises, try to mix your attention with it for as long as possible.

If your mind becomes distracted, use your breath to draw your attention into the present moment and renew your contemplation until equanimity arises again.

Alternate between reflection and concentration. Keep refocusing until the time comes to bring the session to a close.

As your practice concludes, intend to take the mind of equanimity into the rest of your day. Dedicate all the positive energy from your training so that you can accomplish this.

...

As with all the practices, it takes time to gain insight and see changes in our life. We are developing emotional intelligence. In our daily life, our mind naturally discriminates towards the people we encounter. They are either someone whom we like, dislike, or have neutral feelings towards; we try to step back from these habitual thoughts. We can observe how this discrimination causes an imbalance within our mind and relationships.

We mentally retreat, so we can observe how the mind sometimes exaggerates the liking of someone; as a consequence, we will be prone to the disliking of others. Mentally we pull people towards us and push others away. Due to being influenced by these strong emotions, we will be in a mental cul-de-sac where we will have no choice but to ignore the masses.

The mind of equanimity helps us to have an active, positive outlook towards others that is balanced and focused, looking for good qualities. When we train in equanimity, we are cultivating a feeling of warmth towards our self and others. Due to gaining familiarity with the friendly attitude of equanimity, we can start to enjoy balanced inner happiness and build a solid foundation for the subsequent mindful heart practices, such as loving-kindness and compassion.

...

Affectionate Love

Three practices to warm the heart and
strengthen our relationships

Once we have started to train in equanimity, we have a suitable foundation for cultivating the mind of affectionate love. We try to develop a feeling of closeness and intimacy towards others; not just a liking of them, but a feeling of warmth.

Generally, there is confusion surrounding the mind of love. It can be a word that we may feel uncomfortable with and have trouble expressing. We can even be in a relationship with someone for many years and be unclear about our feelings towards them. Perhaps unable to show our emotion and unsure whether we 'love' the person.

Although used in our language, culture, songs, and poetry, there can be a lack of clarity around the word. It is almost as though there is a mystery around the use of the word, making it difficult to use and understand its true meaning.

When we are practising the mindful heart, we are interested in cultivating the mind of love and growing it within our consciousness, independent of how others feel about us.

When we use the word 'love', we are merely referring to a mind that feels close to others and wishes for them to be happy, without needing or expecting anything in return.

Feeling affectionate love for others and sharing our good heart brings well-being and good fortune into our lives.

Affectionate love helps to steer our mind in a positive direction so our relationships will be meaningful, and so our heart can be filled with balance and warmth.

Let us engage in a reflection and meditation where we can start to develop this mind and explore how we can integrate it into our daily life.

It is helpful to recognise and appreciate that we already have affectionate love. The emotion is not new for us. The meditations presented here are simply encouraging its growth.

...

Meditation One
Recalling someone with affection

Begin your practice by bringing your attention into the present moment, through developing a mindful awareness of your body and breathing.

Follow the sensation of your breath as it enters and leaves your body.

Try to develop a single-pointed concentration and abide calmly with your breathing.

Recall somebody in your life that you hold with affection.

Imagine them next to you. Explore this emotion of affection.

As it arises within your mind, try to develop a focus, so your attention is solely with this affection.

When you develop affectionate love, you are cultivating the emotion within your heart, not your head.

Try not to focus too much on the person that you have affection for, but instead explore and stay with the mind.

When your attention becomes distracted, try to notice immediately and encourage affectionate love to return.

If you completely lose the object of your meditation, then gather your awareness and connect with your breath for a short time, to refocus your mind. After this, go through the above contemplation again.

Engage in this process of contemplation and concentration for as long as possible.

When you are ready to finish the practice, make the determination to integrate and carry affectionate love into the rest of your day and life.

...

Meditation Two

Including more people in our heart

In this practice follow a similar process as mentioned above.

Draw your attention to the breath, to focus and tune your mind.

Recall someone whom you feel affection for, imagining them next to you.

Allow the mind of affection to arise within your consciousness.

Then try to bring more people from your life into the visualisation.

Try to extend the feeling of affection that you have toward them.

Hold this good heart with your focus.

It is natural that some of the relationships you have in your life are challenging and difficult. Try gradually to see beyond the faults, and instead focus on the kindness you have received, so you can allow yourself to generate affection.

Extend the feeling of affection out further, to include as many people as possible, engaging in the following contemplation:

'All these people are just like me. They have been born into the human world and have to undergo all the challenges of having a human body and mind, they all have to endure uncertainty and confusion.'

Reflecting like this, we develop an affinity with others' situations and circumstances, which helps us to develop affection for them.

When the mind of affection arises, try to focus your single-pointed attention on it for as long as possible.

If your attention wanders, immediately bring back the mind of affection.

If you lose your object of meditation entirely, use the breath to refocus your mind until you are ready to develop affection.

Meditating on affectionate love will bring great positive energy to your life. Before you finish your meditation, dedicate the training so that you can continue practising in daily life.

...

Meditation Three

Remembering the kindness we receive

Another method for cultivating affectionate love is to remember the kindness that we receive.

We tend to follow habits of mind, when we are alone and when we are with others. As presented in the equanimity training, we hold either pleasant, unpleasant, or neutral feelings towards others, making us feel close to some, distant from others whose faults we see, and indifferent towards everybody else.

These habits of mind can lead to feelings of neutrality and indifference, an autopilot approach to our thoughts and emotions, we can let them arise, and we believe what they tell us. When we interact with others, whether it is physically, verbally, or mentally, we automatically generate states of mind towards them.

In this next method for developing the mindful heart, we focus on recognising the kindness we receive from those around us, thereby enabling the cultivation of a positive mind that overrides our ordinary discrimination.

❖

Bring your attention to the present moment and focus on the natural sensation of your breath, calmly abiding.

Keeping the practice simple and clear, reflect on everything that you have received from others in your life thus far:

The body you currently have.

The clothes that you wear.

The language you use to communicate.

The food inside your stomach.

The ability you have to walk, to balance.

All the skills you have been taught throughout your life.

Your friends, family, and colleagues who have assisted you.

Your opportunity to work and carry out all the other tasks that fill your day.

The transport systems you enjoy.

The health within the body you currently have.

I present a short list but, if you wish, add more kindness from your personal experience.

When you think of those around you, it can be easy to forget the kindness you have received from them.

If you can remember the kindness that you have received from others, then you have the basic thought-structure for being able to develop affection.

Remembering gratitude helps to bring life and energy into your mind of love.

Allow love to arise in your mind towards others and try to mix your attention with it for as long as possible.

Use your breath to bring your attention into the present moment if your mind wanders, and this will help you to stay focused and refresh your mind of love.

As the session concludes, make the intention to carry this positive attitude into your daily life.

...

As our meditation progresses, we will start to have more confidence and strength in our mind. Over time as our practice develops, we can begin to try and cultivate an affectionate love for those who challenge us in some way, recognising they are helping us to practise patience, tolerance, and compassion.

With this mental attitude, our outlook when we see and think of others is positive; therefore, when we are with them, our mind uplifts and naturally our relationships improve. Our mind follows its habit. So, if we tend to see faults in others, then this habit will continue to arise. However, this does not mean that these thoughts need to stay and our habit is unchangeable.

When we go out into our world, mentally we try to remember the kindness that we are continuously receiving. In this way, our life can start to become a meditation on love; the mindful heart will organically grow as we interact with others.

This training does not mean that we become weak, and others will start to take advantage of us. Far from it. Affection brings positive energy and power into our mind, strengthening our confidence to pursue our beneficial intention.

When love grows in our mind, our mental health naturally increases, and we become happier. Through training in the mindful practices contained within this book, we can cultivate emotional intelligence, which helps us to step back from the intense emotions that fly through our mind.

We cultivate a mindspace that provides us with the opportunity to decide how we respond to emotions. When we see the faults that we assign to others arise in our mind, we let them arise, step back and then let them go. They can begin to leave our mind naturally, and we can start to stop their influence.

Our thoughts are just like clouds passing through the sky. We do not have to believe that the views are correct or should be followed, just because they are arising in our mind. With skilful mind training, we can begin to let them dissolve. With regular practice, we can start to replace the mind that sees faults in others, with the mind of affectionate love that sees their kindness.

It is natural that with some people it is more challenging than others. However, it is essential to make a start and not be discouraged.

When a novice weight-trainer commences, they do not begin by lifting the heaviest weights. Likewise, when we start training in the mindful heart, we begin by lifting the lighter weights. For those people whom we find it relatively straightforward to develop affection towards, we firstly extend our heart towards them.

Gradually, patiently, over time, we increase our capacity, so that we can include more people inside our mindful heart. It is our freedom whom we choose to include inside our mind of love. Even with a little training and a gentle extension of the heart, there will be a considerable benefit for us, and the people in our life.

With consistent training over a prolonged period, it is possible to include countless individuals within our mind. The more love we can generate, the happier we feel inside, and the more satisfying our relationships will be.

...

Cherishing Love

Increasing our good heart by seeking
out others' good qualities

Each of the practices in the mindful heart training leads naturally into the next. When we see, hear, and think about others, with equanimity, we can maintain a calm, relaxed, balanced mind. We start to develop the emotional intelligence that is required to help us step back from busyness and distractions by beginning to observe thoughts, as though they were clouds passing through the sky of our mind. This skill is possible but takes time.

Once we can start to identify negative thoughts, we begin to let them pass and provide ourselves with the option to replace them with alternatives, such as the mind of equanimity; liking others, feeling close to them, and seeing oneself as a potential friend to anyone who needs one.

Thus we can build our relationships, both physically and mentally. The quality of a relationship does not just depend on how much time we spend in the company of a person. More subtly, the way in which we think of them when we are not in their presence also plays a part. Once we have established the ground of equanimity, we then start to cultivate a feeling of affection towards those around us, beginning with those who are close to us and then gradually extending further into our society and the world.

As we extend our mindful heart towards others, we will encounter both inner and outer obstacles. The approach to overcoming these is to love, stronger, deeper, and longer. The way we can do this is by cultivating the mind of cherishing love, then loving kindness and finally compassion.

When encountering obstacles in our relationships, we may be tempted to turn away from others or close our heart, and only open it to those who have 'special' access. Sometimes it is necessary to step away from a relationship, but it may be possible if our mind is suitably trained to open our heart further and defeat the negative with our love.

One question which can arise at this point is: 'What if I get hurt during this process?' If we check carefully, we can see that the hurt we have to go through mentally in our relationships does not arise from the mind of love; it comes from our attitude. The more we can cultivate equanimity and love the more strength we will have in our mind.

A skilful meditation practice helps us to have a better relationship with our self, so we can be comfortable and happy when we are on our own. With this mental health, our relationships with others will naturally improve, becoming healthier and more satisfying. For this to become a reality, we have to keep practising.

When we cultivate cherishing love, we think and are more aware of others' presence in our world. We spend time reflecting on how their happiness, health and success is important. Just as we naturally feel our happiness is special, we now regard others' happiness in the same way.

Naturally, we regard some people who are close to us as unique, but towards those whom we don't know there is little feeling. It requires conscious, continuous training to be able to see the happiness of those whom we do not know, and finally those whom we do not like, as relevant. With familiarity, it is possible and can become a reality for us.

If we can send our mindful heart and thoughts to others, it starts to change our attitude and mind. In our society, we say, 'my heart goes out to you' when expressing compassion towards another. Training in the mindful heart encourages this to happen more. Through seeing others' happiness and freedom as important, we can start to see them as precious. We direct our mindful heart to them and cherishing love will naturally arise.

Through seeing someone as precious, we naturally want to look after them. This state of mind is cherishing love. We cherish others and wish for them to be happy. The great Buddhist meditator, Shantideva, said in his classic text, the Guide to the Bodhisattvas Way of Life:

'All the happiness in the world comes from thinking about others.'

We have a natural instinctive view that cherishes our self and wishes for those close to us to be happy and protected. Here we are building on this natural view and extending it to include many more people. The further we can extend this mind, the more power we have in our internal world, and the better our relationships become. We encounter problems in our connections with others when we do not have this attitude. Cherishing others helps to resolve this issue.

When we see, hear or think about others we direct the thought, with the feeling of love:

'May you be happy, may you be free from problems and difficulties'.

We reflect on these words while cultivating a loving state of mind.

To have success in the mindful heart, we need the foundation of a stable, happy mind which arises from having experience with the previous mindful practices.

If we think rationally and broadly, one person's happiness is good, but surely we can include more than just one or two? As Captain Spock stated in his final few words:

'The needs of the many outweigh the needs of the few.'

...

Loving-Kindness

Discovering a peaceful way of life

The loving-kindness practice is the culmination of the previous mindful heart training. We try to train in this continually. Being both loving and kind brings peace to our life and peace to the world.

Although loving-kindness is a soft, warm heart, it is not a weak approach. We become mentally strong through this training. The more mental strength we can develop through our mindful practices, the greater our ability becomes to solve daily problems as they arise.

Loving-kindness is the expression of our mindful heart. When we encounter others, we feel close to them and have positive thoughts; we see them as special and important and regard their happiness and freedom as significant as our own. We also develop a strong wish that they may find joy in their lives, and act to try and help them in whatever way possible.

Everyone is unique, so to know how to help them requires wisdom and insight, depending on the individual's personality, inclinations, and tendencies.

With the loving-kindness practice, we extend our mindful heart to others. We try to cultivate and integrate the attitude in a practical manner so that we are ready to help if others need us.

Loving-kindness encourages a willingness and strength to go out of our way to try to bring a little happiness and peace into the lives of others.

When we train in loving-kindness, we are developing one of the most positive attitudes that we possibly can. As mentioned in the section on equanimity it is common to have a neutral attitude. It is the most natural thing in the world to follow our regular mental habits. When we practise loving-kindness, we are consciously and actively developing the mindful heart throughout the day.

We can engage in our daily actions of walking, cooking, washing, cleaning, and working, with a mindful awareness of being in the present moment, flavoured by loving kindness. So, we start to change our intention from a neutral approach to one of loving kindness. When we engage in any action, we can ask ourselves the open-ended question: What is my intention?

Sometimes we can be unsure of our intention. Other times we perhaps have a neutral intention. When we are training in the mindful heart, we keep an eye on our intention. We appreciate that it takes time to change, but we can make progress, with a little self-encouragement. As we are engaged in our actions we think:

'May others find freedom and happiness in their lives.
My intention for engaging in this action is so
everyone can find peace and happiness.'

Even a simple action such as preparing food or washing our body can be engaged in with the intention of loving-kindness. With this attitude, we start to transform our actions from neutral to positive. Our actions become positive because our intention is; consequently, we derive all the good results that come from our beneficial actions. Initially, it requires encouragement and regular reminders to turn on the intention of loving-kindness as we need to counteract our autopilot mind.

With familiarity, the training becomes natural and more straightforward to integrate and practice. As a result of fuelling our intention with loving-kindness each day, positive energy will come into our mind, body, relationships and life. Our interactions naturally improve, develop and grow. We can enjoy having the source of true happiness within our mind.

Let's try a simple practice to help encourage this beautiful mind. Please note in this practice we try to include as many people as possible; be as inclusive as you can depending on your capacity and wish.

Bring your attention into the present moment and gradually start to follow the sensation of your breath. Calmly abide.

Focus on the inhalation and exhalation of breath.

Allow the mind to settle and gather inwards.

Start to imagine yourself surrounded by friends and family.

Gradually start to include all the people in your life, then everyone in your society and across your world.

Bring your attention to the heart chakra.

With your mind in this location, develop the wish that those surrounding you may find happiness and good fortune in their lives.

Allow the mind of love to arise. Mix your attention and concentration with it for as long as possible.

Try to become one with this mind.

If the feeling fades, remember the contemplation to renew this mind.

If you find it challenging to cultivate this mind, then bring to mind the feeling of love that you have for one person close to you.

Remember the feeling that you have, let this arise and try to hold it in your mind. If you feel comfortable in doing so, start to extend this mind of love to include more people.

Try and hold the mind of loving-kindness for as long as possible.

Abide with the mind of love in meditation. Try to become one with this emotion.

When you are ready to finish your practice, make the determination to carry the precious mind of loving-kindness into your daily activities.

Arise from your practice with this good heart.

Integrating loving-kindness into our daily life will have incredible, transformative consequences.

...

Compassion

Extending and increasing our good heart

If we are interested in deepening our practices further, we can progress to the next meditation in this series of mindful heart practices, which is training in compassion. Compassion is a mind that observes both our self and those around us with loving-kindness and wishes for us all to be peaceful, happy, free from problems and difficulties. Then through checking carefully, we discover that even though we wish for happiness and to be free, we have to encounter many issues in our life.

Uncertainty, separation, loss, confusion, sickness, ageing and finally death – everyone without exception must encounter these challenges. Nobody wakes in the morning wishing for suffering, problems and difficulties, but we know issues will arise every day.

We can possess all the material objects we could ever desire, but still not feel rested and content. With new acquisitions, we potentially encounter new problems and difficulties. Reflecting in this way, we firstly develop compassion for our self and hold this for a short time. We then extend our compassion to those around us. Calmly abide with this feeling. Gradually we extend our compassion to everyone in our society and across the world.

We start close to home and slowly extend our mindful heart of compassion outwards to include as many people as possible. Compassion is a state of mind that we naturally have, and is an extremely confident and outgoing expression of our heart.

If we see somebody fall over and collapse in the street, we instinctively go to help, due to the mind of compassion. It is not long before a group of people surround them, their compassion driving them to be of assistance to relieve the suffering that they are witnessing.

When people choose careers, they often base their choice on the mind that wishes to reduce the suffering in the world, revealing a compassionate and noble wish. Respecting and acknowledging the existence of this mind will be a cause for it to ripen in our heart. If we are not mindful and forget to tend to the seeds of compassion, it is easy for this positive intention to cloud over the deeper we go into our work, and the more distracted we become by the process, routine and structure of the organisation.

The compassion meditation encourages us to sustain our mindful heart, develop, nurture, and express it during our daily life, so it will increase and grow like a waxing moon.

How do we meditate on compassion? Recalling the final meditation from the third chapter on mindful breathing, we engaged in a practice known as compassionate breathing. Here we were introduced to training in the mind of compassion, focusing on the inhalation and exhalation of our breath.

As we breathe in we develop the wish that we can find freedom from suffering and problems; as we breathe out, we develop the wish that others may find this freedom too. We try to maintain these minds as we stay focused on the sensation of the breath. We can also engage in the following reflection and concentration.

Notice the natural sensation of the breath entering and leaving your body

Visualise your close family and friends next to you.

Surrounding them, visualise all the people that you have met and interacted with throughout your life.

Reflect how, although we all wish to be free from problems and difficulties, each day we have to encounter them without choice.

Reflect how many people in the world don't have access to clean water, food, and basic sanitation.

Everybody has to undergo hardship, frustration, and disappointment.

Even if we have material comfort, we still have to go through the mental hardship of frustration and dissatisfaction from which possessions cannot protect us.

Sometimes mental pressure can be greater, the more material success we achieve.

Reflecting like this in the peace and calm of meditation, encourage the mind of compassion to arise:

'May we all find freedom from problems and difficulties.'

Try to extend this to as many people as you can. Start with yourself, and then include those who are closest to you. Gradually spread this good heart outwards as far as you possibly can.

When this mind of compassion arises clearly in your meditation, try to hold it with single-pointed concentration for as long as you can.

Use your breath to refocus if your mind wanders and becomes distracted

Before the practice ends generate the intention to try and carry this precious mind into your daily life, so whenever you have an interaction with anyone, whether physical, verbal, or mental, you can extend to them, the mindful heart of compassion.

...

All these mindful heart practices encourage us to bring positive energy to our relationships. Each time we revisit them, not only will our heart and mind benefit, so will all the people in our life. If some practices feel too challenging to engage in, initially leave them to one side.

Firstly build up the mindful training from the text that resonates. Over time, when we have enough strength and confidence in our mind, we can start to extend our practice to others using the mindful heart meditations presented in this chapter.

The mindful heart training can be challenging, however, by just starting gently and keeping a positive mind we will witness the beneficial effects of our practice, and feel encouraged to continue and progress. If we have a courageous mental attitude and can extend it outwards, we will see our relationships improve and our progress along the mindful path naturally empowered.

CONCLUSION

We have trained in a series of eight mindful practices. As we progress through the book, our experience builds gradually. As mentioned in the introduction, this book follows the same format as the eight-week beginner course that I present both in the live and online classes. The content here gives more detail and provides further practices beyond the scope of what I deliver in the set of eight one-hour sessions.

Each training leads naturally into the next. If you have read the book and engaged with the content, there may be practices that resonated with you; if so, revisit and practise again. You may feel there is a practice you can continue with on a regular basis, or it may be that you choose to work through the book again and train in the series of meditations, step by step.

When I went through my training in the Buddhist monastery, I attended beginner courses repeatedly. Why was this? To try and keep the beginners' mind attitude, open, humble and always ready to learn. This approach is ideal for entering the world of meditation and has been encouraged by the great Zen masters throughout history. If each time we train we can arrive with a fresh attitude then we will discover the great depth and potential within our mind.

Try to revisit the practices many times, then each time you will gain more insight and benefit. This process of discovery can be likened to when you return to your favourite city.

For example, I go to London perhaps six times a year and have done since I was a little boy. Each time I go, it is new and fresh, maybe I go to a new park, a new café, a new area, see something in a new way, or have a new encounter.

We can have the same experience with these practices if we can approach them in an open, positive, and confident manner, instead of having the mind that thinks, 'I have been there,' or 'I have done that'. Each time we start, we can begin anew, with fresh eyes.

In the first half of this book, we learned an essential mindful practice, helping us to abide in the present moment, in an open, non-judgmental way. We brought our attention into the present moment through **listening** to the sounds around us. Focusing our mind in a relaxed manner, we observed our **body** and the sensation of our **breath**. Then we went deeper, by watching the **mind** itself, stepping back from the thoughts that continually arise.

These are the practices from the first four chapters. By skilfully combining these mindful trainings, we learn an essential daily meditation that helps us abide in the present moment.

In the second set of four chapters we explored how to integrate our mindful meditation into daily life; firstly through bringing awareness to the **movement** and **flow** of our actions. Remembering to be mindful when we eat, slows down our life, triggers the ability to practice in our daily activities, while also facilitating good physical health.

Using the training before and during our **sleep** encourages us to rest well and dream peacefully. We learn how to let go consciously, at the end of each day and during the night, which enables us to wake refreshed and uplifted. Finally, the mindful **heart** training assists us in having a compassionate awareness with others, thus enhancing and strengthening our relationships.

Through practising the instructions shared in this book, we can cultivate peace within our mind and consequently be at peace with the world around us.

Once we have completed the training presented here, we have created the foundation for then exploring the Mindspace+ series of courses and books. In this extensive programme, we focus on themes such as gratitude, patience, fearlessness, compassion, wisdom, and concentration. Please see the next steps chapter, for more information.

Mindful meditation helps us to see the intimate relationship between our mind and the world that appears to it, meaning we can start to appreciate that each time we develop one, we will naturally enhance the other. This understanding will give us the confidence and enthusiasm to put effort into training our mind, recognising that the most powerful way we can improve and change the world, is to cultivate and transform our mind.

The mindful practices presented here encourage us to take a positive interest in each moment of our life. If we engage with them regularly, we will be empowered to extract the greatest meaning from our human existence.

I wish you all the very best with your training and invite you to get in touch via the Mindspace website with any questions you may have concerning your practice.

CONDENSED VERSION

If you are short of time and wish to go straight to the practices, then try reflecting on the verses below which summarise the content contained within the chapters of the book.

LISTEN

Become aware of the sounds around you.

Bring yourself to the moment.

Allow any thoughts of the future and past to dissolve.

As you listen, gather your attention.

Listen to the closest sounds.

Slowly gather your mind.

Gently listen to your breath.

Carefully and openly, abide.

...

BODY

—

Observe the body.

Feel your feet against the ground.

Notice lightly.

Bring your attention inwards.

Become one with your body.

Let it anchor you to the moment.

Abide.

Carry this awareness into your day.

...

BREATH

Become aware of your breath.

Notice the sensations.

Just observe, without control.

Abiding.

Enjoy the natural flow.

Remember through your day.

Breathe.

...

MIND

—

Turn to the mind itself.

Deeper than distraction.

Go to the clarity

The ocean, beyond the waves.

Allow thoughts to pass.

Just sit.

Just watch.

Expect nothing.

...

MOVEMENT

———

Standing upright and relaxed.

Place your hands near the navel.

Observe.

Abide.

Breathe in.

Lift your foot, take a step.

Breathe out, place your foot down.

Walk softly and slowly.

Breathe with each step.

No rush.

...

FLOW

———

Take a breath and prepare your tea.

Cherish the movement.

Observe yourself, observe the flow.

Notice the smell, the steam...

Slow down.

There is no hurry.

Your mindful energy; a gift to the world.

Smile quietly and taste.

...

SLEEP

Relax on your back.

Place both hands on your stomach.

Bring all your attention to them.

Settle here.

Follow the rising and falling.

Let your thoughts pacify.

When you wander, return to the hands.

Making peace with yourself and the world.

With your breath go to sleep.

Dream sweet.

...

HEART

———

Reflect:

May I be free from problems and difficulties.

May others be free from problems and difficulties.

Then bring your attention to the natural breath.

As you breathe in reflect on the first wish.

As you breathe, out the second.

Then as you breathe, focus on both wishes.

Carry this compassion into the rest of your day.

...

NEXT STEPS

Deepen your experience on the Mindspace+ programme

Mindspace+: Build the foundation for a deeper practice

Improving our Relationships with Loving Kindness:
Practices to enhance our communication and mental peace

Improving Concentration: Meditations to help improve focus

Zen Mindfulness: Minimising clutter and strengthening our ability to be in the present moment

Wisdom: Developing insight and inner peace

Gratitude: How to uplift the mind and encourage inner joy

Patience: Learning how to keep a calm and stable mind

Fearlessness: Reducing obstacles, increasing confidence

Compassion: Meditations to nourish our incredible potential

Happy: How to keep a happy, positive mind

Freedom: Leaving negativity behind & enjoying mental freedom

For more details, please visit:
www.mindspace.org.uk/mindspace-online

ACKNOWLEDGMENTS

This book has arisen in dependence upon countless people. I send an ocean of gratitude to all the teachers that I have been fortunate to encounter through my life. To all those within the monasteries and Buddhist centres I have lived in, who have shown an inspirational example and generosity of wisdom, bows of thanks are eternally offered.

Before departing for Asia, my philosophy and psychology teachers, Alan McEachran and Quintin Pond, introduced me to the world of the mind and how to reflect objectively; thank you for this. Even though I was not a model student, I am continuing to benefit from your words. Teachers come in many guises, and I am grateful for all who have guided me.

Thanks to my dear mum, Joan, who showed me that having a positive and happy attitude comes from learning to watch the world go by, being kind to 'strangers', and having a sense of joy for the small things in life. I dedicate this book to her memory. She lives on within the words and practices contained in this text. With my sister Mary and her two beautiful children, Melissa and Isabella, we will continue to manifest all the goodness that you have shared. Thank you to the generosity of the Devi family, your kindness will never be forgotten, and of course, to Sapna.

Whenever I start a new course I say to the students attending, although I am sitting in the teacher's chair, I am also a student. Each time I teach, I learn from the students' feedback, questions and input. A teacher and students existence depend upon each other. They are equal, and the positions are interchangeable. Therefore, I appreciate you taking the time to read this book and look forward to meeting, hearing, and learning from you! I also encourage, that if you have benefited from the practices, to share them with your friends and family.

I wrote this text over the course of two years, often utilising the generous space of coffee shops in the cities and towns where I was residing. Appreciation and thanks are offered to the following locations and staff for providing an ambient and relaxing space to reflect, focus, and write; oh and also all the delicious coffee and occasional slice of cake!

Peace Oriental Tea House: Bangkok
Ngopi Coffee: Birmingham
Colour Brown Coffee: Hong Kong
Quarter Horse Coffee: Birmingham
Hungry Bird Coffee: Bali
Faculty Coffee: Birmingham
Starbucks Reserve: Bangkok
Waylands Yard: Birmingham
Habitual Coffee: Manila
Filosofi Kopi: Jakarta
Lime Tree: Tettenhall
Paludan's Book & Cafe: Copenhagen
Hungarian Pastry Shop: Upper West Side, NYC
Wari Coffee: Koh Chang

...

NOTES

———

Preface
xiii: Location of retreat was Kopan Monastery, Kathmandu.
xiv: Quote from Shantidevas, Guide to the Bodhisattvas Way of Life. Library of Tibetan Works and Archives, Dharmshala, India

Mindful Listening
Page 2: For live beginner classes: www.mindspace.org.uk/start

Mindful Movement
Page 88: Plato's Cave Analogy for more information:
www.en.wikipedia.org/wiki/Allegory_of_the_Cave
Page 90: Shunryu Suzuki teaching is taken from the text:
Zen Mind, Beginners Mind.
Page 98 & 99: Quotes from Henry David Thoreau's Walden:
Read more here: en.wikiquote.org/wiki/Walden

Mindful Flow
Page 122: Find out more about Noma here: www.noma.dk
Page 132: Meditation in Schools website resource page:
www.meditationinschools.org
Page 146: Mindspace app can be downloaded here:
www.mindspace.org.uk/app

Mindful Sleep
Page 153: Buddha referred to is in Wat Pho
(Temple of the Reclining Buddha), Bangkok, Thailand.

Conclusion
Page 189: Please get in touch: www.mindspace.org.uk/contact